Name

Darrionv

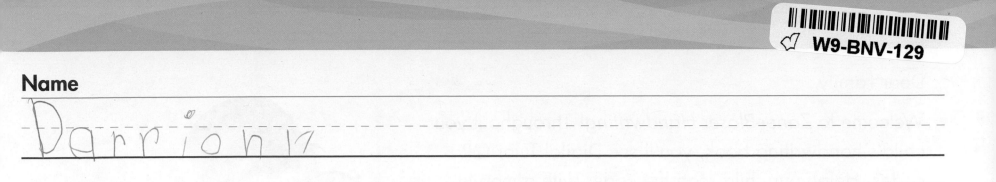

Zaner-Bloser
Handwriting

1

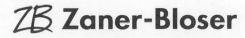

ZB **Zaner-Bloser**

A Highlights Company

Dear Family,

Welcome to *Zaner-Bloser Handwriting*! Throughout your child's handwriting book, you'll see Digital Tutor QR codes. Help your child scan the codes with a mobile device to access instructional videos that reinforce the basics of handwriting and how to write letters and numerals. Turn to page 1 for more information.

Occupational Therapy Consultants

Asha Asher, MA OTR/L, FAOTA, MEd (Special Education), Redlands, CA
Carol Armann, OTR/L, Marietta, OH

ELL Consultants

Ellen Riojas Clark, PhD, Professor Emerita of Bicultural-Bilingual
  Studies, University of Texas at San Antonio
Patricia Sánchez, PhD, Professor of Bicultural-Bilingual Studies,
  University of Texas at San Antonio

Reviewers

Julia Ann Agard, University of Nebraska at Kearney, NE
Jeffrey Armann, Frontier Local School District, OH
Ramona Blair, Bellwood School District 88, IL
Denise Brosius, Caesar Rodney School District, DE
Dr. James Troutman, Ed.D., University of Houston, TX
Kathy Twaroski, Ashwaubenon School District, WI
Valerie White, St. Anne's Episcopal School, Middletown, DE
Iefay A. Williams, School District of Philadelphia, PA

ISBN 978-1-4531-1928-0

This book is printed on paper certified by third-party standards for sustainably managed forestry.

Zaner-Bloser, Inc.
800.421.3018
zaner-bloser.com
Printed in the United States of America

2 3 4 5 6 7 8 9 10 11 997 24 23 22 21 20 19   ZB Code 20

Table of Contents

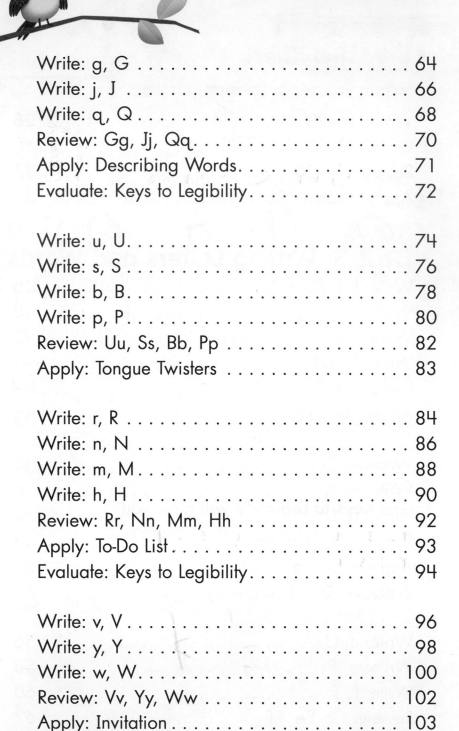

Unit 4: Using What You Have Learned

Meet Zaney

Zaney will be popping up in your book to help you form letters and make sure your writing is easy to read!

Digital Tutor

Scan the **Digital Tutor** codes with a mobile device to watch Zaney's videos. You will learn how to write your best letters!

Digital Tutor

Introduction

Models and Guidelines

There are writing models in your book. The models are on guidelines.

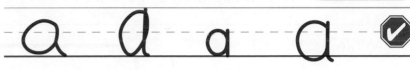

- Headline
- Midline
- Baseline
- Descender Space

The red arrows and numerals show you how to write each letter.

Start at the green dot when you trace and write.

Digital Tutor

Writing on the Lines

Stop and Check

When you see a ✓ sign, circle the best letter you wrote on that line.

Circle the best letter on this line.

Digital Tutor

Stop and Check

$a \quad a \quad a \quad a$ ✓

Keys to Legibility

There are four kinds of keys in your book. These **Keys to Legibility**™ will remind you to check the **Shape**, **Size**, **Spacing**, and **Slant** of your writing.

The **Keys to Legibility** will help you make your writing legible. **Legible** means easy to read.

Digital Tutor

Keys to Legibility

Pretest

Write your name here.

Darrion

Write how old you are here.

6

Write letters you know here.

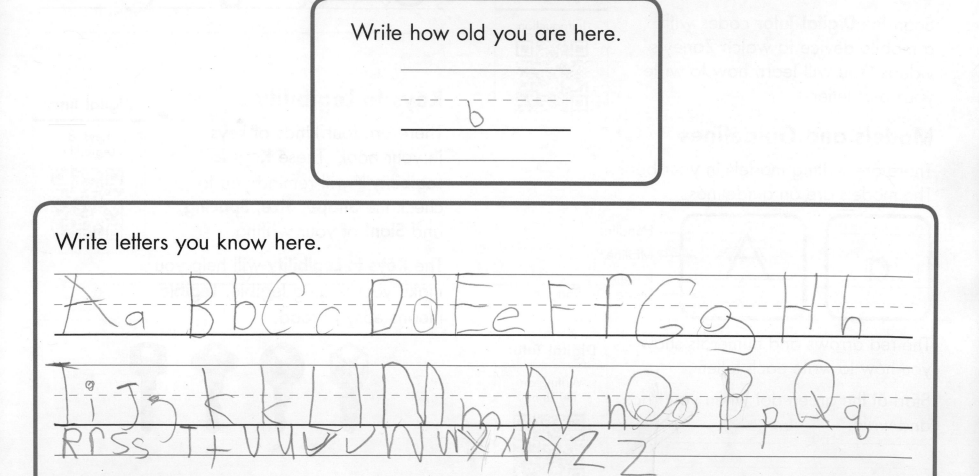

Aa Bb Cc Dd Ee Ff Gg Hh
Ii Jj Kk Ll Mm Nn Oo Pp Qq
Rr Ss Tt Uu Vv Ww Xx Yy Zz

Show what else you can write here. Draw a picture about your writing.

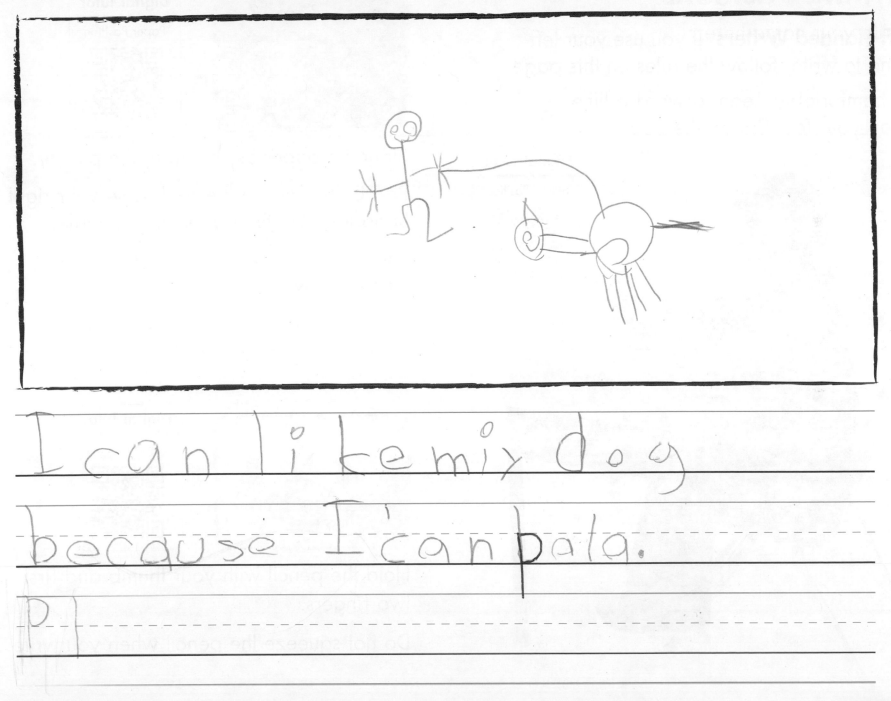

I can lite miy dog
because I can pala.
P

Writing Positions

Left-Handed Writers If you use your left hand to write, follow the rules on this page.

Sit comfortably. Lean forward a little. Keep your feet flat on the floor.

Digital Tutor

Paper Position

Slant the paper as shown in the picture.

Rest both arms on the desk. Use your right hand to move the paper as you write.

Pull the pencil toward your left elbow when you write.

Digital Tutor

Sitting Position

Digital Tutor

Pencil Position

Hold the pencil with your thumb and first two fingers.

Do not squeeze the pencil when you write.

Right-Handed Writers If you use your right hand to write, follow the rules on this page.

Sit comfortably. Lean forward a little. Keep your feet flat on the floor.

Digital Tutor

Paper Position

Place the paper straight in front of you.

Rest both arms on the desk. Use your left hand to move the paper as you write.

Pull the pencil toward the middle of your body when you write.

Digital Tutor

Sitting Position

Digital Tutor

Pencil Position

Hold the pencil with your thumb and first two fingers.

Do not squeeze the pencil when you write.

Basic Strokes

Vertical Lines Some letters and numerals have lines that are straight up and down.

Trace the straight up and down lines in these letters and numerals.

H D E t b i 9 4

Trace the vertical lines in the picture. Start at the green dot. ● Stop at the red dot. ●

Trace and write. Pull down straight. ✓ Circle your best vertical line.

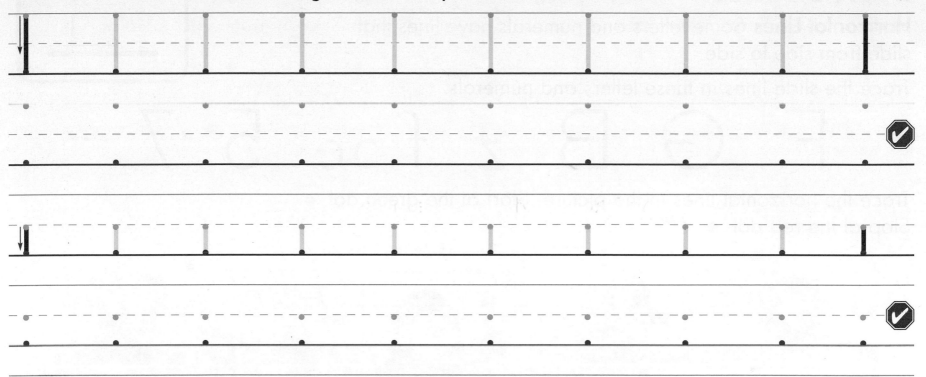

Trace and write. Push up straight. ✓ Circle your best vertical line.

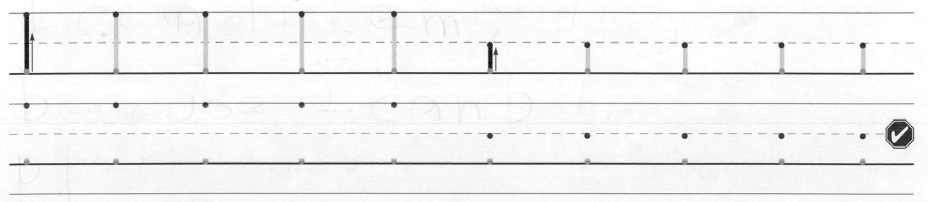

Basic Strokes

Horizontal Lines Some letters and numerals have lines that slide from side to side.

Trace the slide lines in these letters and numerals.

F G B z f e 5 7

Trace the horizontal lines in the picture. Start at the green dot. ●
Stop at the red dot. ●

Trace and write. Slide right. ✓ Circle your best horizontal line.

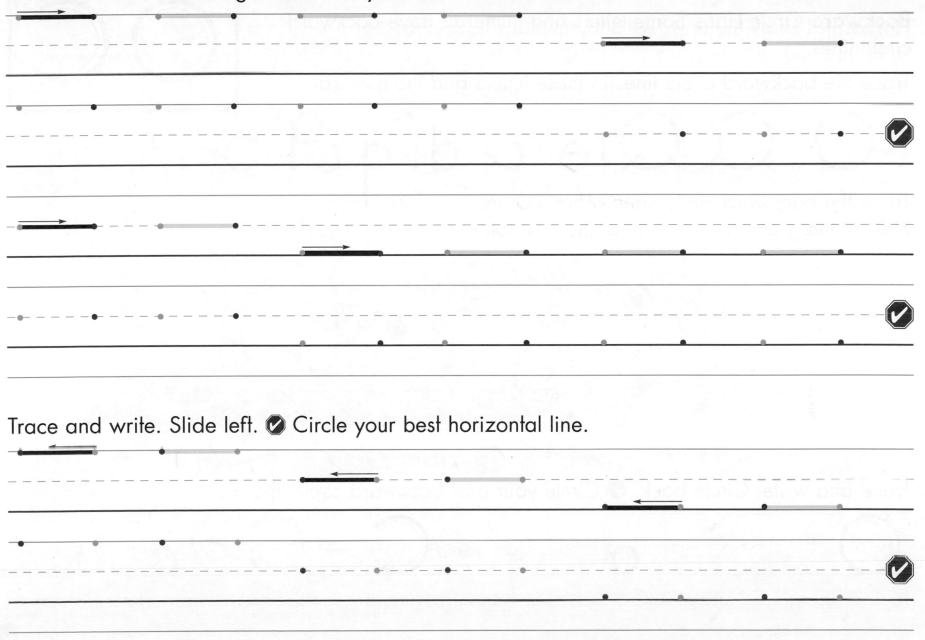

Trace and write. Slide left. ✓ Circle your best horizontal line.

Basic Strokes

Backward Circle Lines Some letters and numerals have backward circle lines.

Trace the backward circle lines in these letters and the numeral.

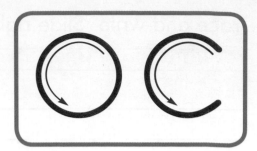

O C Q e c d q 9

Trace the backward circle lines in the picture.
Start at the green dot. ● Stop at the red dot. ●

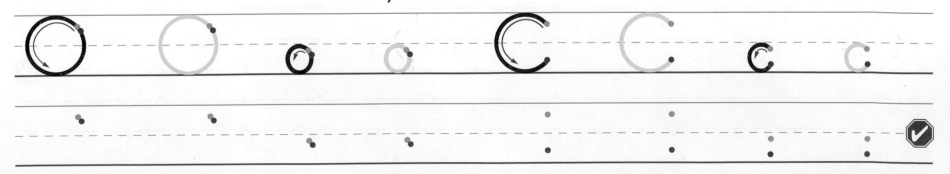

Trace and write. Circle back. ✓ Circle your best backward circle line.

Basic Strokes

Forward Circle Lines Some letters and numerals have forward circle lines.

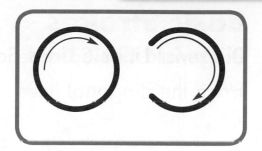

Trace the forward circle lines in these letters and numerals.

R P D b 5 3

Trace the forward circle lines in the picture.
Start at the green dot. ● Stop at the red dot. ●

Trace and write. Circle forward. ✅ Circle your best forward circle line.

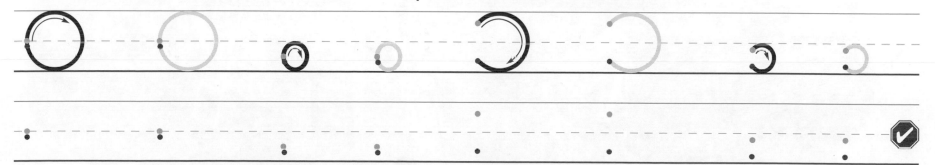

Basic Strokes

Diagonal Lines Some letters and numerals have diagonal lines.

Trace the diagonal lines in these letters and numerals.

A N Q y w z 2 7

Trace the diagonal lines in the picture. Start at the green dot. ●
Stop at the red dot. ●

Trace and write. Slant right. ✓ Circle your best diagonal line.

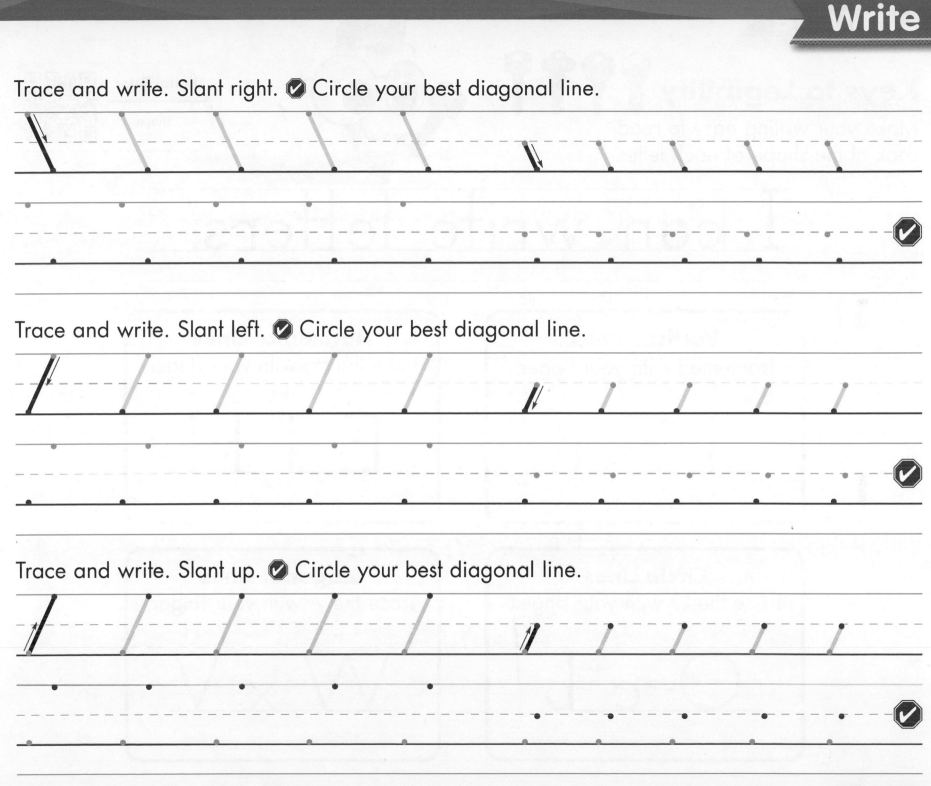

Trace and write. Slant left. ✓ Circle your best diagonal line.

Trace and write. Slant up. ✓ Circle your best diagonal line.

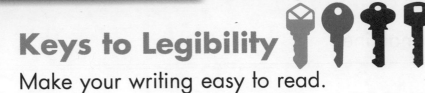

Keys to Legibility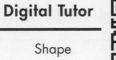

Make your writing easy to read.
Look at the shape of each letter.

Digital Tutor

Shape

I can write letters.

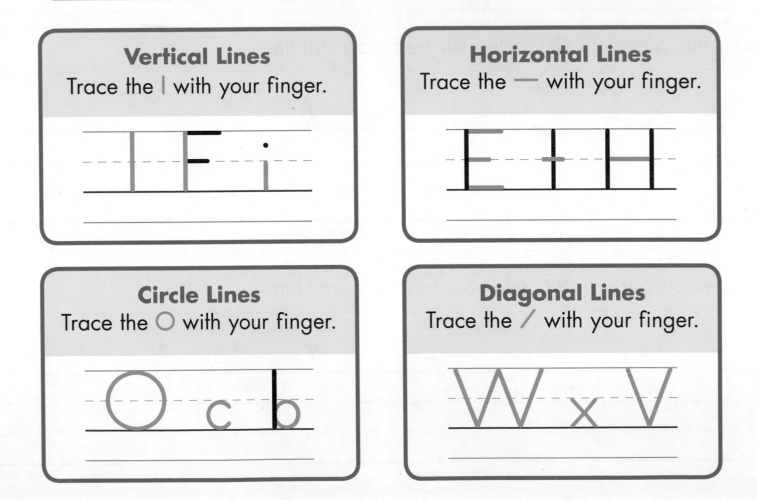

Vertical Lines
Trace the | with your finger.

Horizontal Lines
Trace the — with your finger.

Circle Lines
Trace the ○ with your finger.

Diagonal Lines
Trace the / with your finger.

Trace the | lines in these letters.

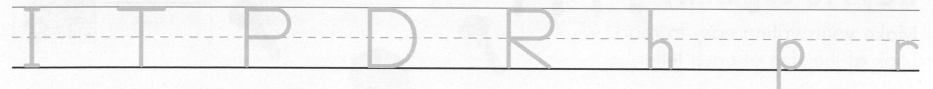

I   T   P   D   R   h   p   r

Trace the — lines in these letters.

E   F   L   H   G   A   e   f

Trace the ○ lines in these letters.

O   C   S   B   c   s   o   q

Trace the / \ lines in these letters.

Q   X   K   M   v   w   x   k

Keys to Legibility

Make your writing easy to read.
Look at the size of each letter.

Digital Tutor

Size

Writing is fun!

Tall Letters
Tall letters touch
the headline.

K b d

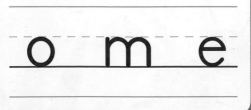

Short Letters
Short letters touch
the midline.

o m e

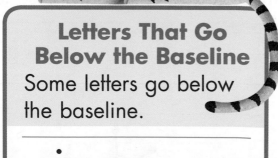

Letters That Go
Below the Baseline
Some letters go below
the baseline.

j g y

Trace and write tall letters. Start at the green dot. ●

T O A L D t d

Trace and write short letters.

a o c i e v r n

Trace and write letters that go below the baseline.

g p j q y

Keys to Legibility

Make your writing easy to read.
Look at the spacing between letters.

Digital Tutor

Spacing

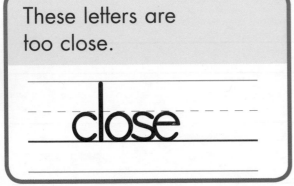

These letters are too close.

close

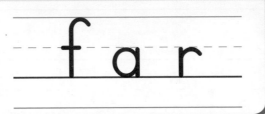

These letters are too far apart.

f a r

These letters have good spacing.

good

Circle the two words with good spacing between letters.

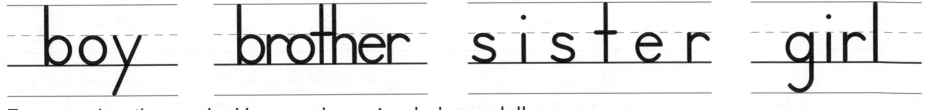

boy   brother   sister   girl

Trace and write words. Use good spacing between letters.

aunts   uncles   cousins

Make your writing easy to read.
Look at the spacing between words. Notice that your finger can fit between each word.

This is just right.

Circle the sentence that has good spacing.

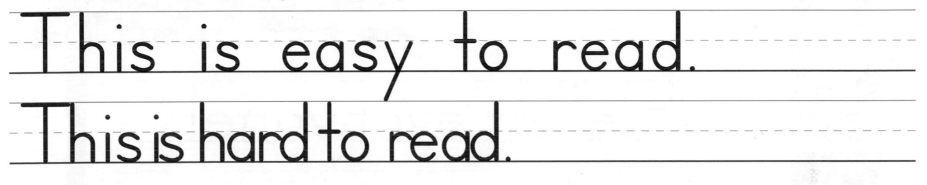

This is easy to read.

This is hard to read.

Write the sentences. Use good spacing.

I can read. I like to read.

Keys to Legibility

Make your writing easy to read.
Look at the slant of the letters.

Digital Tutor

Slant

Hello, everyone!

These letters are straight up and down.

straight

Circle each word that is straight up and down.

smile   smile   *smile*   *smile*

laugh laugh laugh *laugh*

Trace and write the words. Make the letters straight up and down.

giggle   sing   dance

hum   play

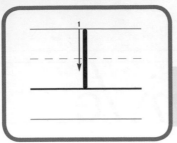

1. Pull down straight.

1. Curve forward; slant left. Slide right.

1. Curve forward. Curve forward.

Trace and write. ✅ Circle your best **1**, **2**, and **3**.

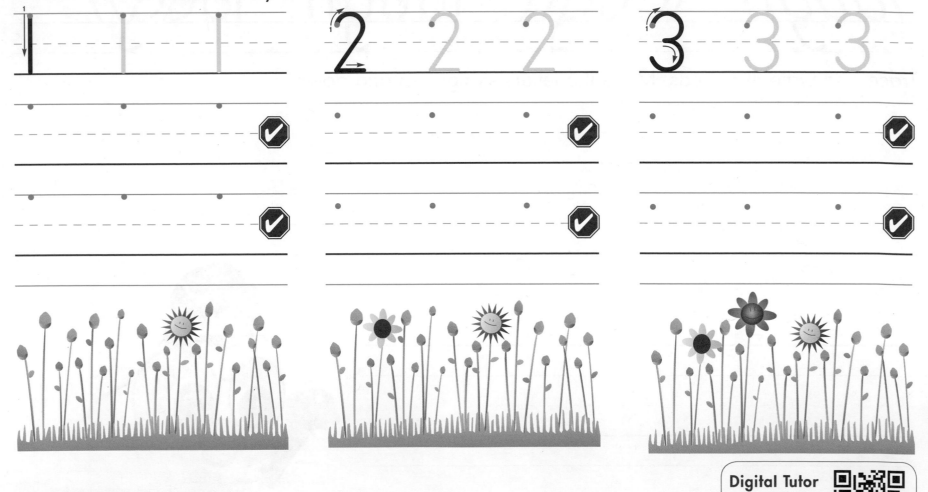

Digital Tutor

Numeral Models and Formations

4

1. Pull down straight. Slide right. Lift.
2. Pull down straight.

5

1. Pull down straight. Circle forward. Lift.
2. Slide right.

Trace and write. ✓ Circle your best **4** and your best **5**.

1. Curve down; curve up and around.

1. Slide right. Slant left.

1. Curve back; curve forward; slant up.

Trace and write. ✅ Circle your best **6, 7,** and **8**.

Digital Tutor

Numeral Models and Formations

1. Circle back all the way around. Pull down straight.

1. Pull down straight. Lift.
2. Curve down; curve up.

Trace and write. ✓ Circle your best **9** and your best **10**.

Digital Tutor

Numeral Models and Formations

Write

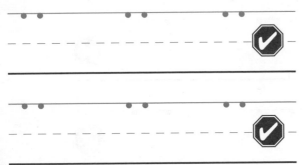

1. Pull down straight. Lift.
2. Pull down straight.

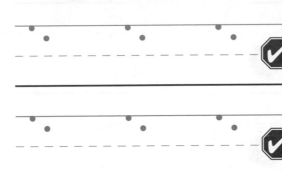

1. Pull down straight. Lift.
2. Curve forward; slant left. Slide right.

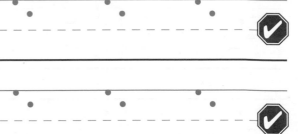

1. Pull down straight. Lift.
2. Curve forward. Curve forward.

Trace and write. ✔ Circle your best **11**, **12**, and **13**.

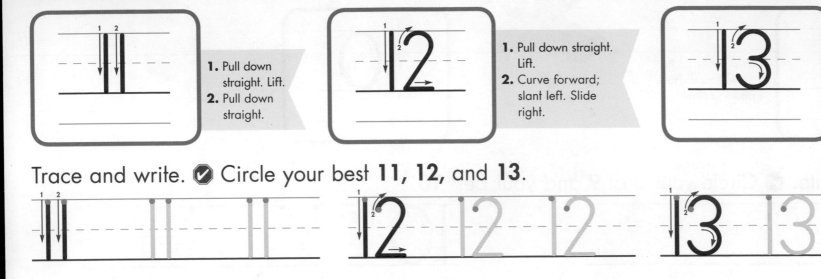

Digital Tutor

Numeral Models and Formations

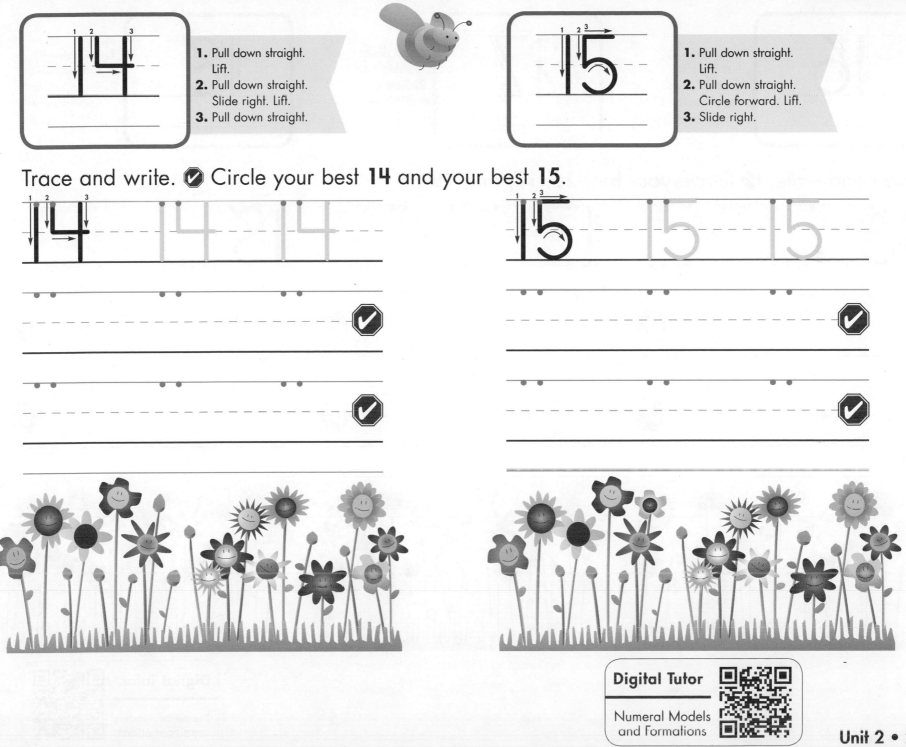

1. Pull down straight.
   Lift.
2. Pull down straight.
   Slide right. Lift.
3. Pull down straight.

1. Pull down straight.
   Lift.
2. Pull down straight.
   Circle forward. Lift.
3. Slide right.

Trace and write. ✓ Circle your best **14** and your best **15**.

Write

16
1. Pull down straight. Lift.
2. Curve down; curve up and around.

17
1. Pull down straight. Lift.
2. Slide right. Slant left.

18
1. Pull down straight. Lift.
2. Curve forward. Curve forward.

Trace and write. ⬡ Circle your best **16**, **17**, and **18**.

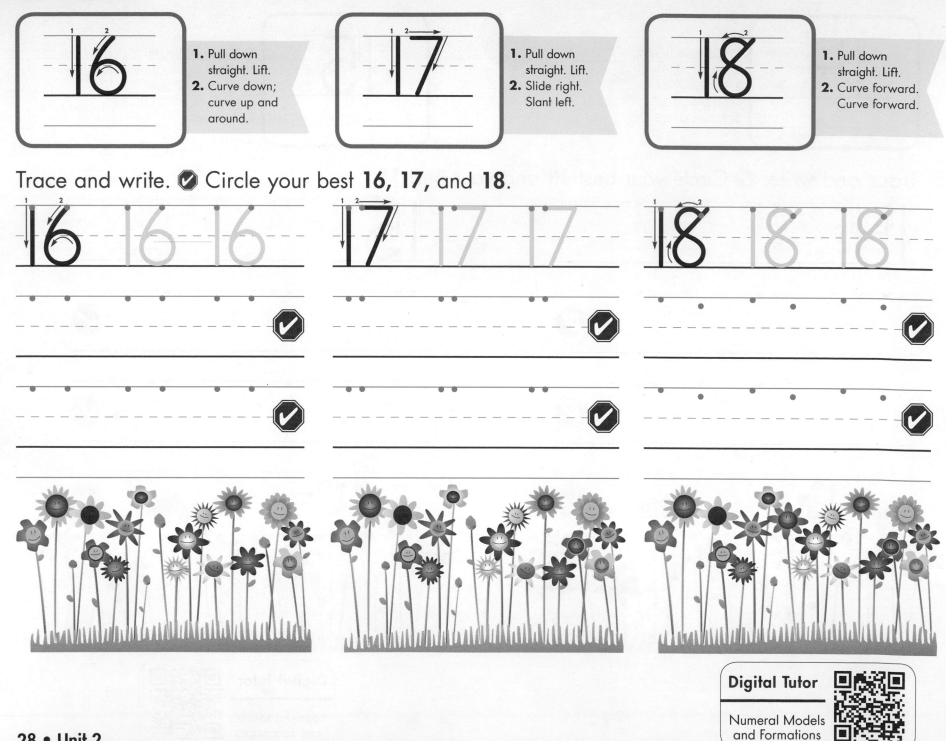

Digital Tutor

Numeral Models and Formations

19
1. Pull down straight. Lift.
2. Circle back all the way around. Pull down straight.

20
1. Curve forward; slant left. Slide right. Lift.
2. Curve down; curve up.

Trace and write. ● Circle your best **19** and your best **20**.

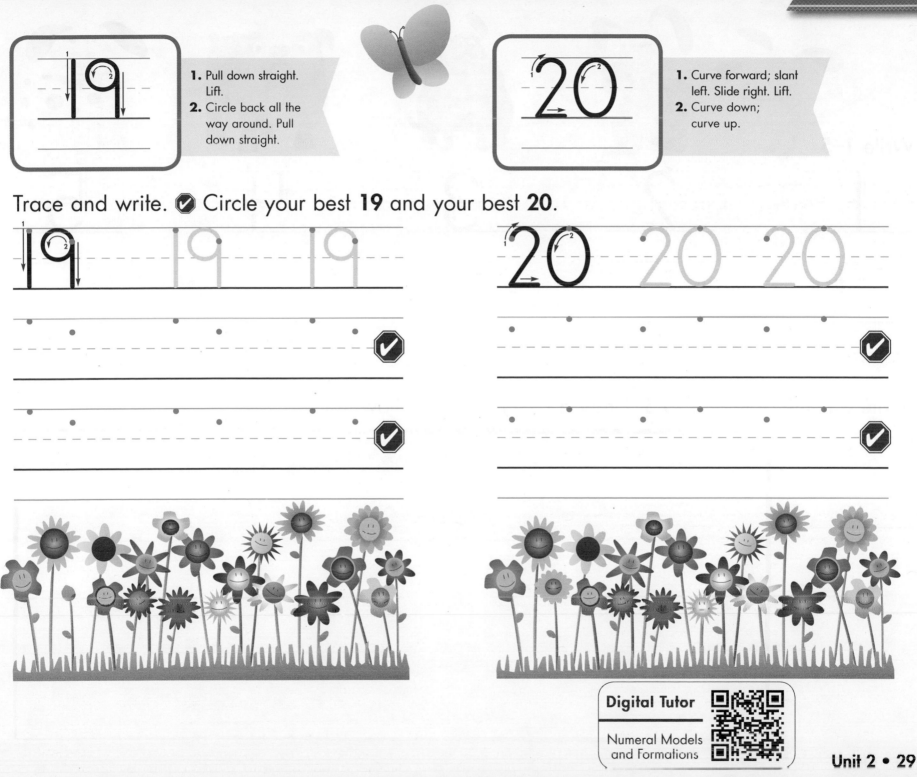

Write **1–5**.

1
2
3
4
5

Write a numeral from **1 to 5**. Draw a picture to show how many.

Write 6–10.

6   7   8   9   10

Write a numeral from **6 to 10**. Draw a picture to show how many.

Write **11–15**.

Write a numeral from **11 to 15**. Draw a picture to show how many.

Write **16–20**.

16   17   18   19   20

Write a numeral from **16 to 20**. Draw a picture to show how many.

Number Sentences Write the number sentences.

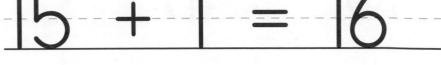

$1 + 2 = 3$

___ + ___ = ___

$15 + 1 = 16$

___ + ___ = ___

$7 + 2 = 9$

___ + ___ = ___

$14 + 4 = 18$

___ + ___ = ___

Write the number sentences.

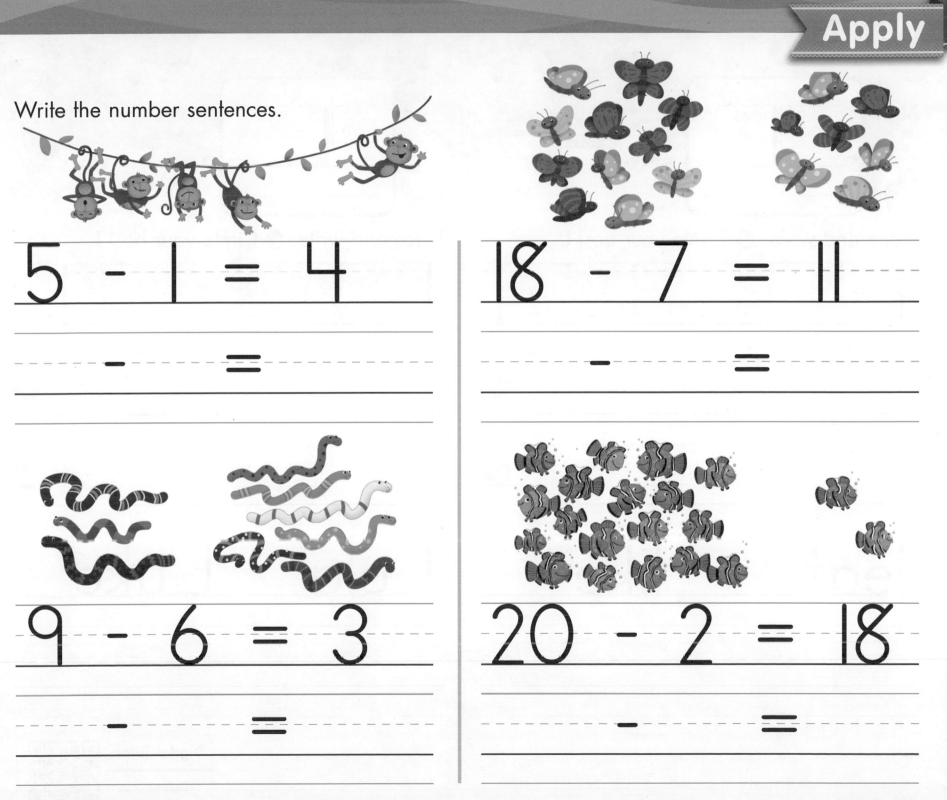

$5 - 1 = 4$

$\_ - \_ = \_$

$18 - 7 = 11$

$\_ - \_ = \_$

$9 - 6 = 3$

$\_ - \_ = \_$

$20 - 2 = 18$

$\_ - \_ = \_$

1. Pull down straight.

1. Pull down straight.
   Slide right.

Trace and write. ✓ Circle your best **l**.

Trace and write. ✓ Circle your best **L**.

leaf   like

Lola   Luke

Digital Tutor

Letter Models
and Formations

Write the words.

long   lake   live   love

Write the sentence.

Look at my letters.

Write a sentence that tells how your letters look.

My letters

Shape Circle your best letter that has a l line.

Write

Trace and write. ✓ Circle your best **i**.

insect   lit

Trace and write. ✓ Circle your best **I**.

1. Pull down straight. Lift.
2. Dot.

1. Pull down straight. Lift.
2. Slide right. Lift.
3. Slide right.

Ivan   Isabel

Digital Tutor

Letter Models
and Formations

Write the words.

inch   ill   into   it

Write the sentence.

I like to write my name.

Write a sentence that tells about something you like to do.

I really like

Write

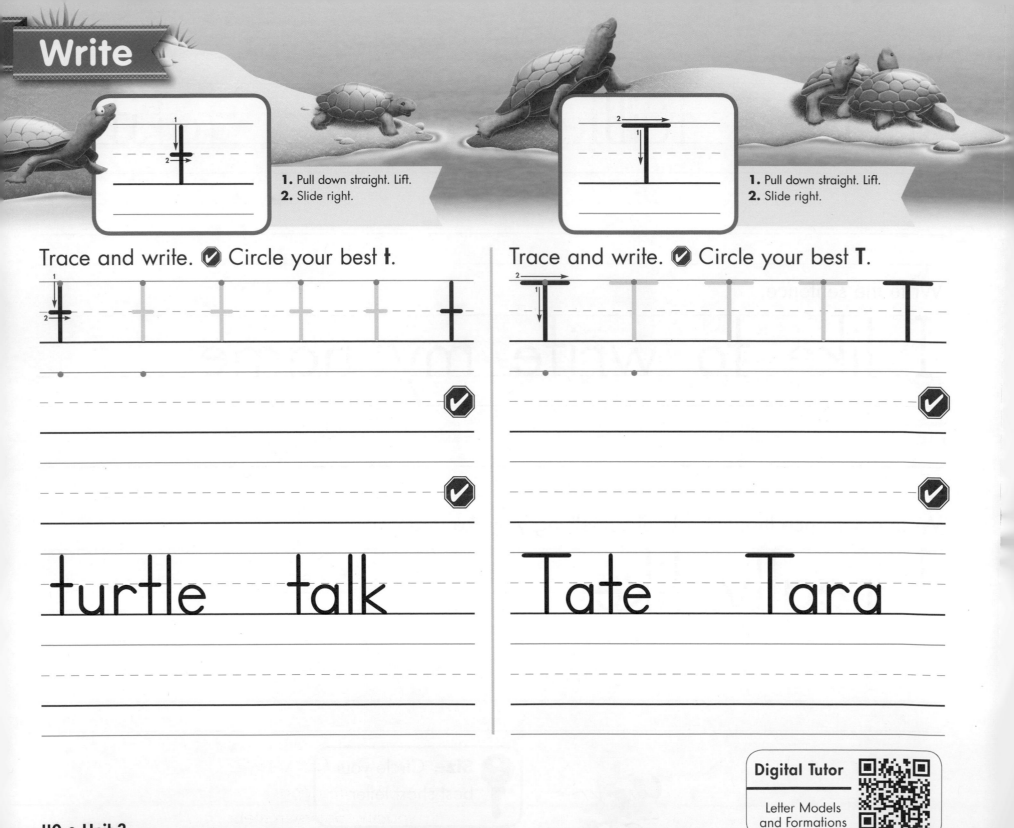

1. Pull down straight. Lift.
2. Slide right.

1. Pull down straight. Lift.
2. Slide right.

Trace and write. ✓ Circle your best **t**.

Trace and write. ✓ Circle your best **T**.

turtle talk

Tate Tara

Digital Tutor

Letter Models and Formations

Write the words.

than   table   tell   take

_____

_____

Write the sentence.

This is my toy train.

_____

_____

Finish the sentence about toy trains.

Toy trains are

_____

_____

Spacing Circle two letters with good spacing between them.

Write

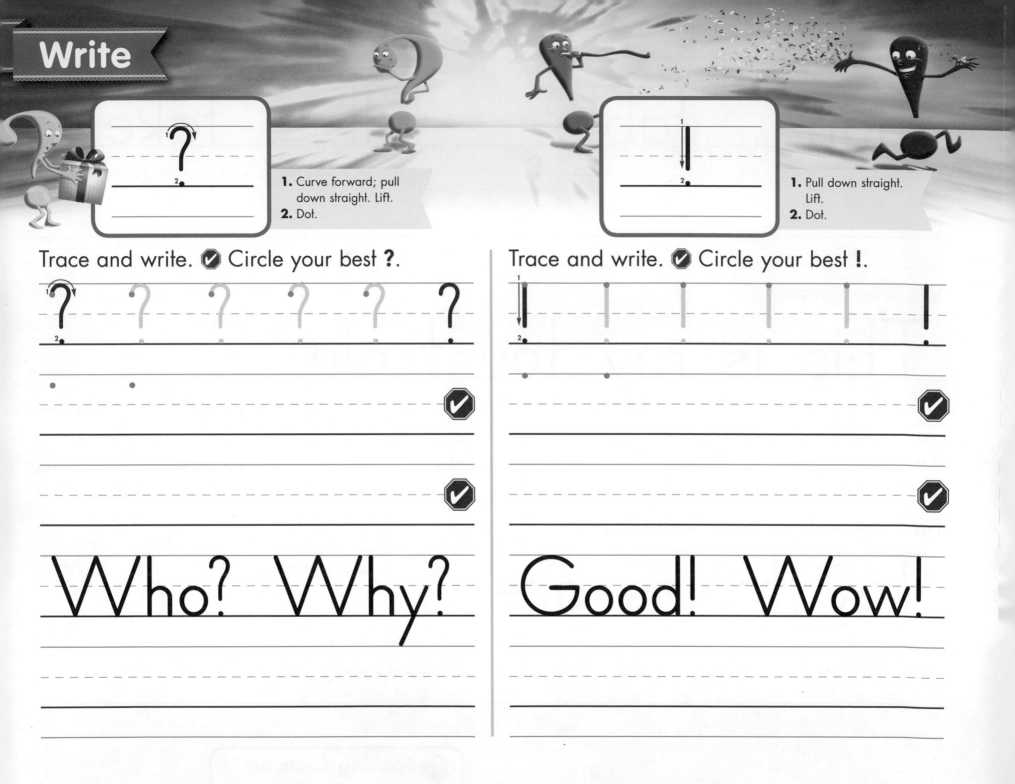

?

1. Curve forward; pull down straight. Lift.
2. Dot.

|

1. Pull down straight. Lift.
2. Dot.

Trace and write. ✔ Circle your best **?**.

? ? ? ? ? ?

Who? Why?

Trace and write. ✔ Circle your best **!**.

| | | | | |

Good! Wow!

Write the sentences.

Can you come over?

I will see you soon!

Write words to finish the sentence.

I like to see

Slant Circle a letter that is straight up and down.

Write the letters and punctuation marks.

l l l l l

i i i i i

t t t t

? ? ? ?

L L L

I I I

T T T

! ! ! !

Write the words.

it   lit   ill   till   little

Sentences Write the sentences.

Look at me!

Today is my birthday.

Am I one year older?

Write a sentence about what you like to do on your birthday.

Write

1. Circle back all the way around.

1. Circle back all the way around.

Trace and write. ✓ Circle your best **o**.

Trace and write. ✓ Circle your best **O**.

otter   hot

Olivia   Ollie

Digital Tutor

Letter Models
and Formations

Write the words.

octopus   off   on   odd

Write the sentence.

Our class took a trip.

Write a sentence about a class trip you have taken.

Our trip was

Shape Circle your best letter that has a ◯ line.

Write

Trace and write. Circle your best **a**.

a a a a a a

a l l i g a t o r   a c t

Trace and write. Circle your best **A**.

A A A A A

A l i   A n n a

1. Circle back all the way around; push up straight. Pull down straight.

1. Slant left. Lift.
2. Slant right. Lift.
3. Slide right.

Write the words.

as   animal   ask   all

Write the sentence.

All my friends play ball.

Write words to finish the sentence.

I can play

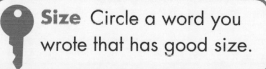

Size Circle a word you wrote that has good size.

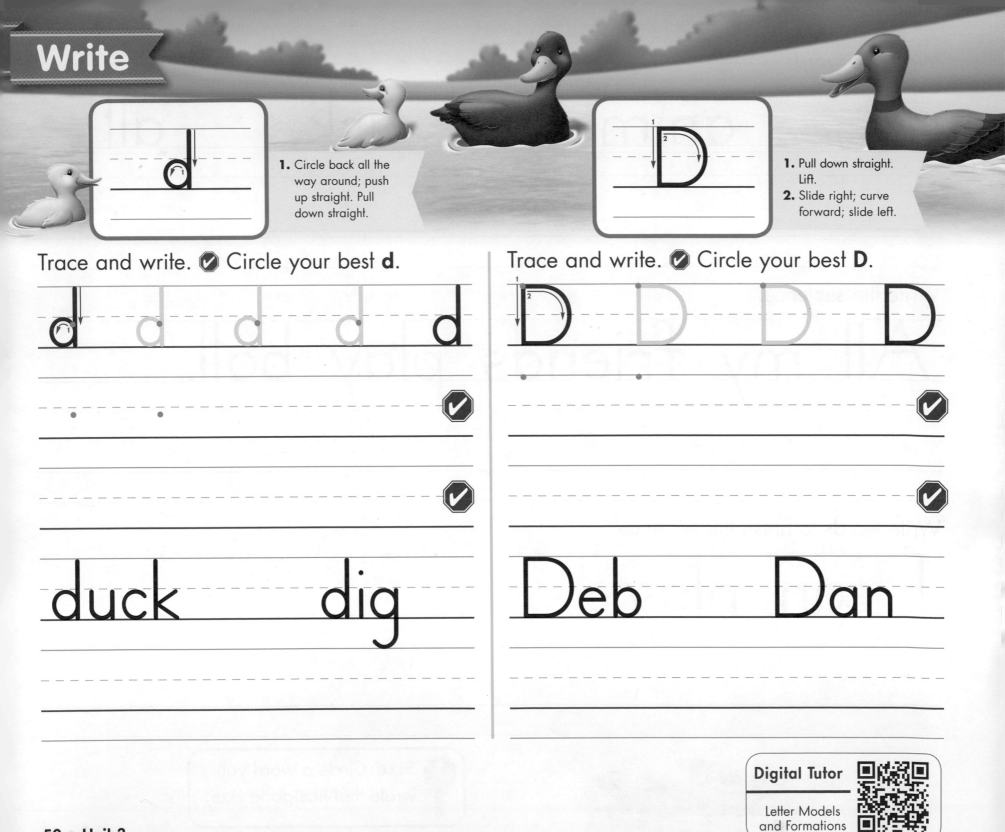

1. Circle back all the way around; push up straight. Pull down straight.

1. Pull down straight. Lift.
2. Slide right; curve forward; slide left.

Trace and write. ✓ Circle your best **d**.

d d d d d

duck   dig

Trace and write. ✓ Circle your best **D**.

D D D D D

Deb   Dan

Digital Tutor

Letter Models and Formations

Write the words.

dad   doll   dress   do

Write the sentence.

Do you like dinosaurs?

Write words to finish the sentence.

Dinosaurs are

Write the letters.

o o o o a a a a d d d d

O O O A A A D D D

Write the words.

odd   add   dad   dot

Naming Words Write the naming words.

dog

toad

Dan

apple

yard

Amy

Write a sentence telling what you like to do with your friends.

Keys to Legibility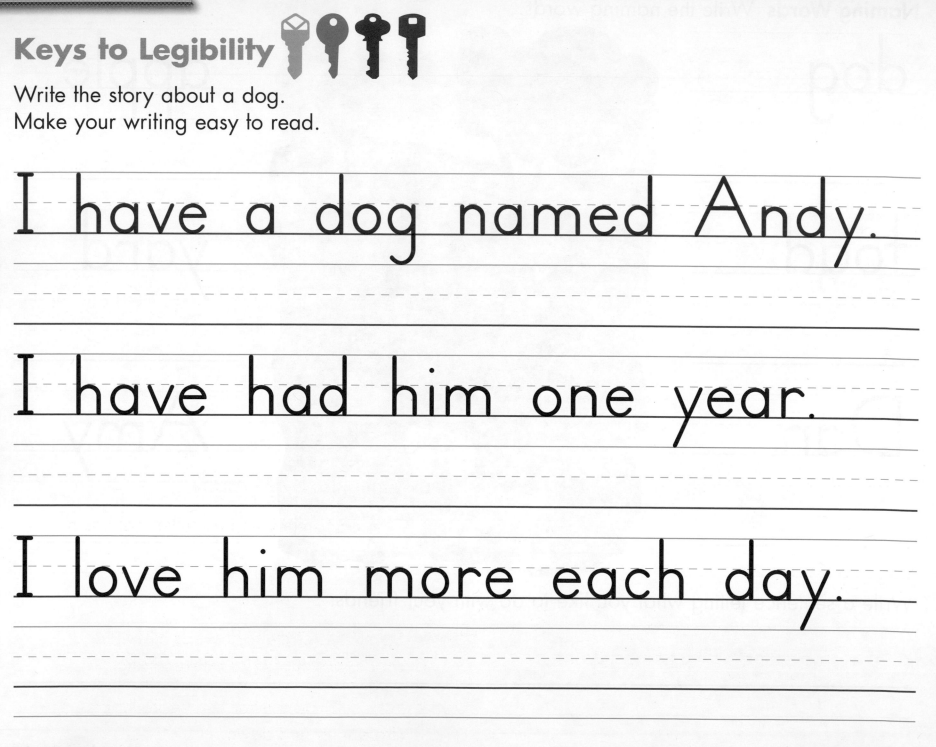

Write the story about a dog.
Make your writing easy to read.

I have a dog named Andy.

I have had him one year.

I love him more each day.

All people should have dogs.

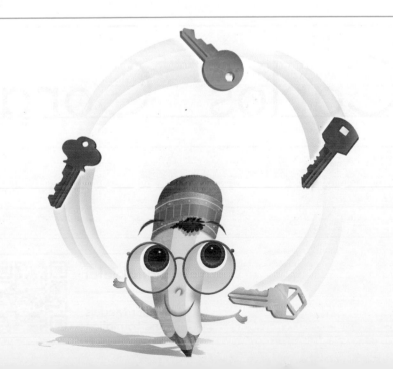

Is your writing easy to read?

 Shape Circle your best letter that has a ◯ line.

Size Circle your best short letter.

Spacing Circle two words that have space for your finger between them.

Slant Circle a letter you wrote that is straight up and down.

1. Circle back.

1. Circle back.

Trace and write. ✅ Circle your best **c**.

c c c c c

✅

✅

car   carry

Trace and write. ✅ Circle your best **C**.

C C C C C

✅

✅

Carlos Cora

Digital Tutor

Letter Models
and Formations

Write the words.

chest   chair   cook   cut

Write the sentence.

Can you count to 20?

Write a sentence about counting.

1. Slide right.
   Circle back.

1. Pull down straight. Lift.
2. Slide right. Lift.
3. Slide right; stop short. Lift.
4. Slide right.

Trace and write. ✔ Circle your best **e**.

e e e e e

elephant eat

Trace and write. ✔ Circle your best **E**.

E E E E E

Ellie Ed

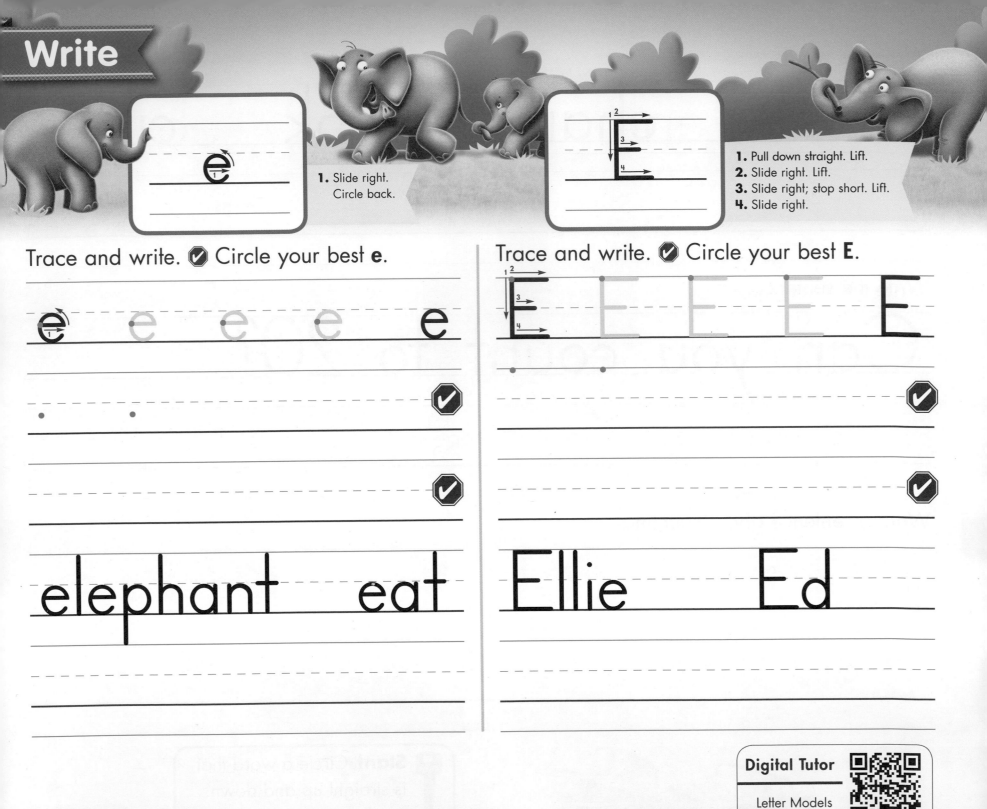

Digital Tutor

Letter Models
and Formations

Write the words.

egg   end   empty   each

Write the sentence.

Everyone enjoys stories.

Write a sentence about something you enjoy.

Shape Circle your best
letter that has a l line.

Write

Trace and write. ✔ Circle your best **f**.

f f f f f

fish   find

Trace and write. ✔ Circle your best **F**.

F F F F F

Fred   Flora

1. Curve back; pull down straight. Lift.
2. Slide right.

1. Pull down straight. Lift.
2. Slide right. Lift.
3. Slide right; stop short.

Digital Tutor

Letter Models and Formations

Write the words.

fun   family   fall   fly

Write the sentence.

Friends have lots of fun.

Write a sentence about your friends.

Size Circle your best tall letter.

Write the letters.

c c c c   e e e e   f f f f

C C C C   E E E E   F F F F

Write the words.

face   feet   ice   life

Action Words Write the action words. ✔ Circle your best letter.

eat

catch

call

fill

feed

color

Write a sentence that tells what you like to do. Use an action word.

Write

Trace and write. ✓ Circle your best g.

1. Circle back all the way around; push up straight. Pull down straight; curve back.

g g g g g

goat go

Trace and write. ✓ Circle your best G.

1. Circle back. Slide left.

G G G G

Grace Glen

Digital Tutor

Letter Models and Formations

Write the words.

girl   gate   goes   got

Write the sentence.

Get ready, get set, giggle!

Write a sentence about something that makes you giggle.

Spacing Circle two words with good spacing between them.

Write

1. Pull down straight; curve back. Lift.
2. Dot.

1. Pull down straight; curve back. Lift.
2. Slide right.

Trace and write. ✓ Circle your best **j**.

Trace and write. ✓ Circle your best **J**.

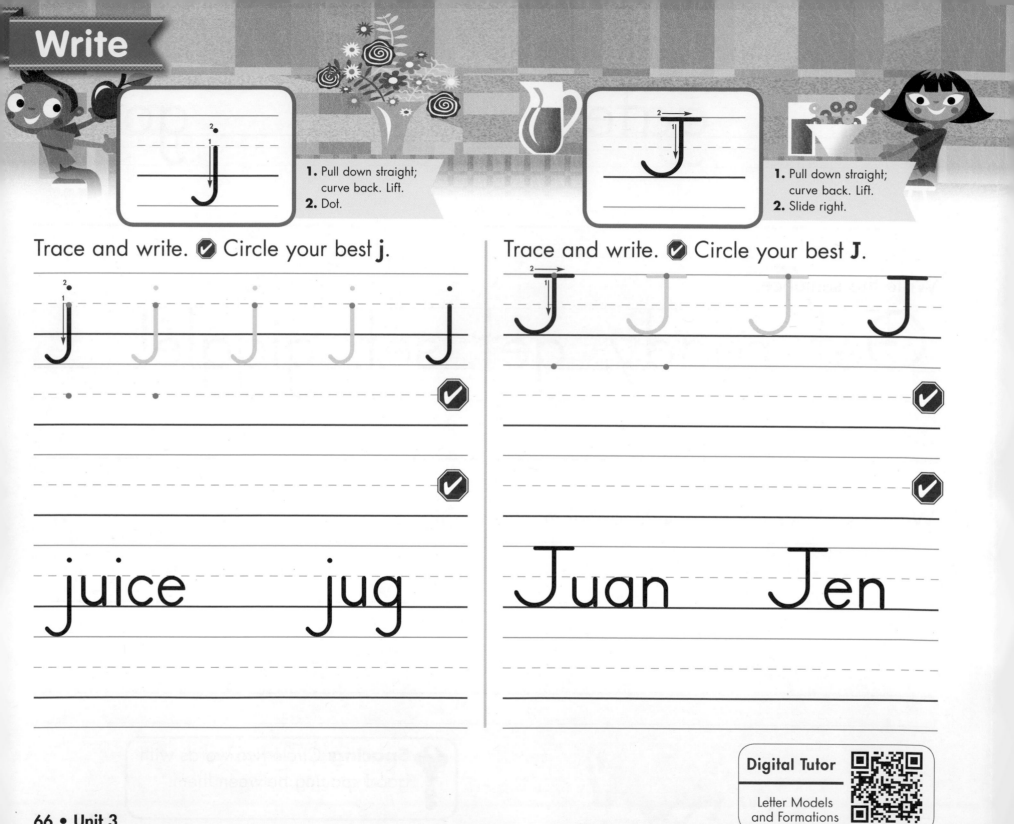

j   j   j   j   j

J   J   J   J   J

juice   jug

Juan   Jen

Digital Tutor

Letter Models and Formations

Write the words.

jam   jar   joke   jog

Write the sentence.

Juice tastes good.

Write a sentence about something that is juicy.

Slant Circle a letter that is straight up and down.

Write

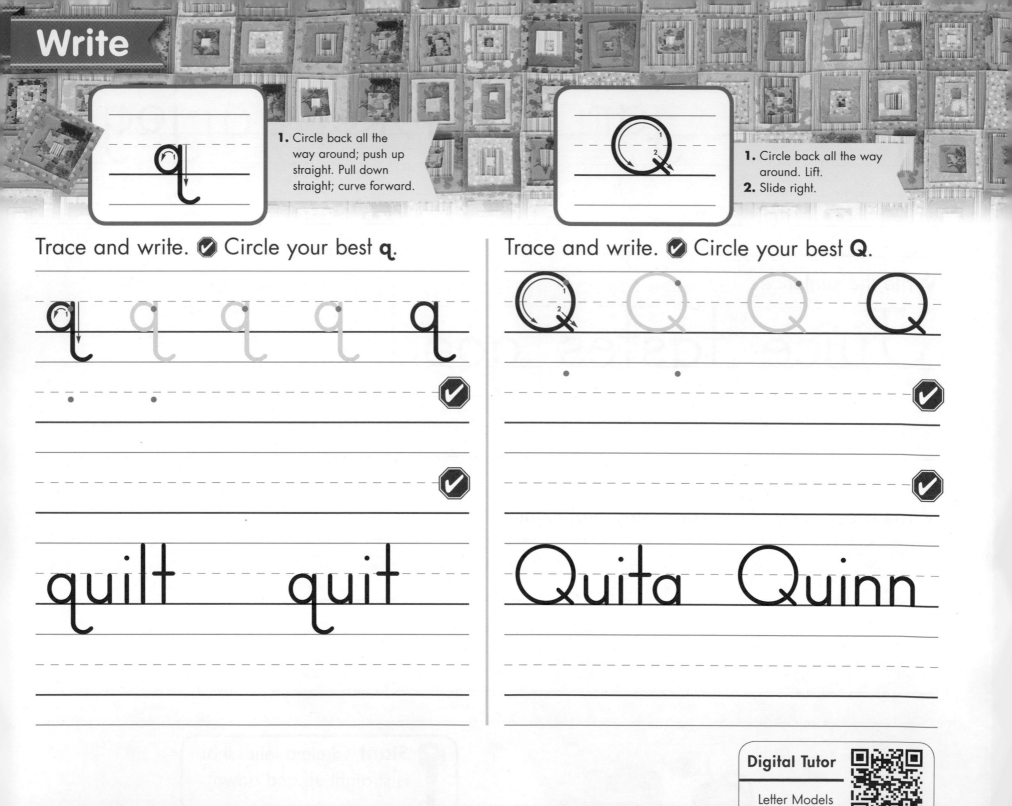

1. Circle back all the way around; push up straight. Pull down straight; curve forward.

1. Circle back all the way around. Lift.
2. Slide right.

Trace and write. ✓ Circle your best **q**.

q q q q q

quilt   quit

Trace and write. ✓ Circle your best **Q**.

Q Q Q Q

Quita Quinn

Digital Tutor

Letter Models and Formations

Write the words.

queen   quart   quarter

Write the sentences. Leave the correct spacing between words and sentences.

Quick! It's time to go.

Write a sentence about doing something quickly.

Shape Circle your best letter that has a ◯ line.

Write the letters.

g g g g g   j j j j   q q q q q

G G G   J J J   Q Q Q

Write the words.

cage   jeans   grass   quite

Describing Words Write the describing words. ✓ Circle your best letter.

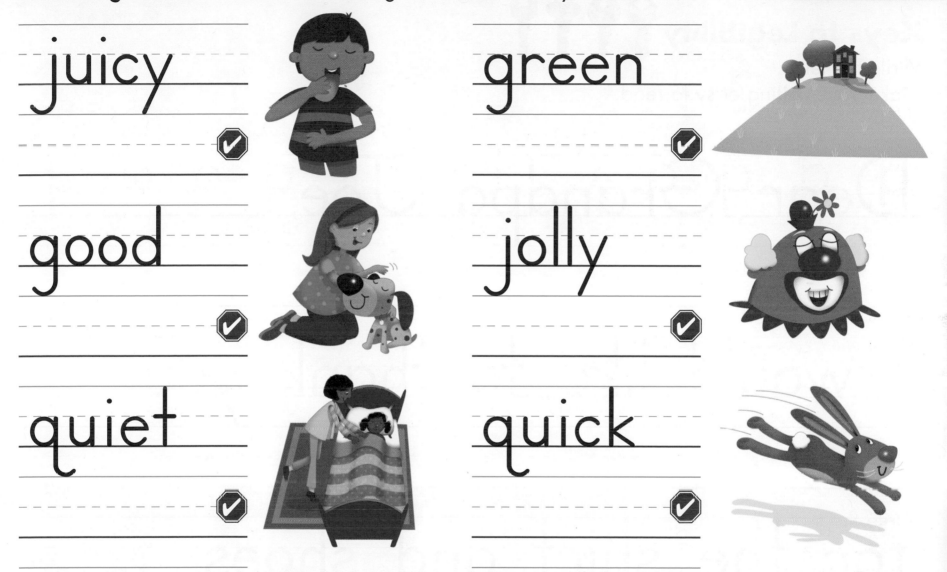

juicy

green

good

jolly

quiet

quick

Write a sentence about something you like. Use describing words.

Keys to Legibility

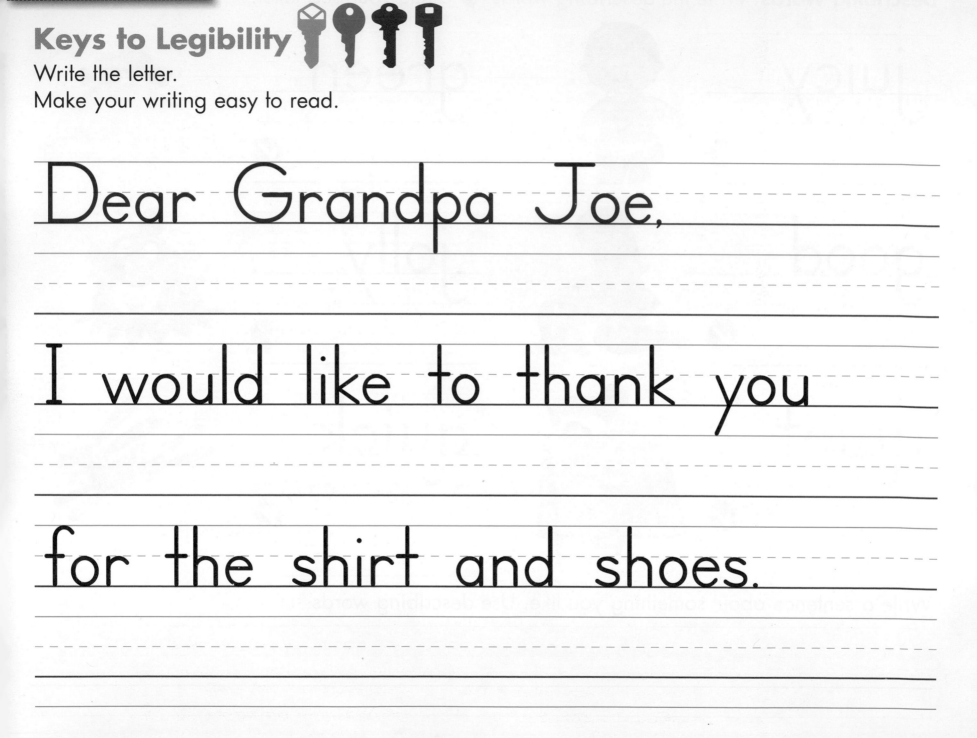

Write the letter.
Make your writing easy to read.

Dear Grandpa Joe,

I would like to thank you

for the shirt and shoes.

Love,

Jorge

Is your writing easy to read?

Shape Circle your best letter that has a — line.

Size Circle your best tall letter.

Spacing Circle two words that have space for your finger between them.

Slant Circle a word you wrote that has good slant.

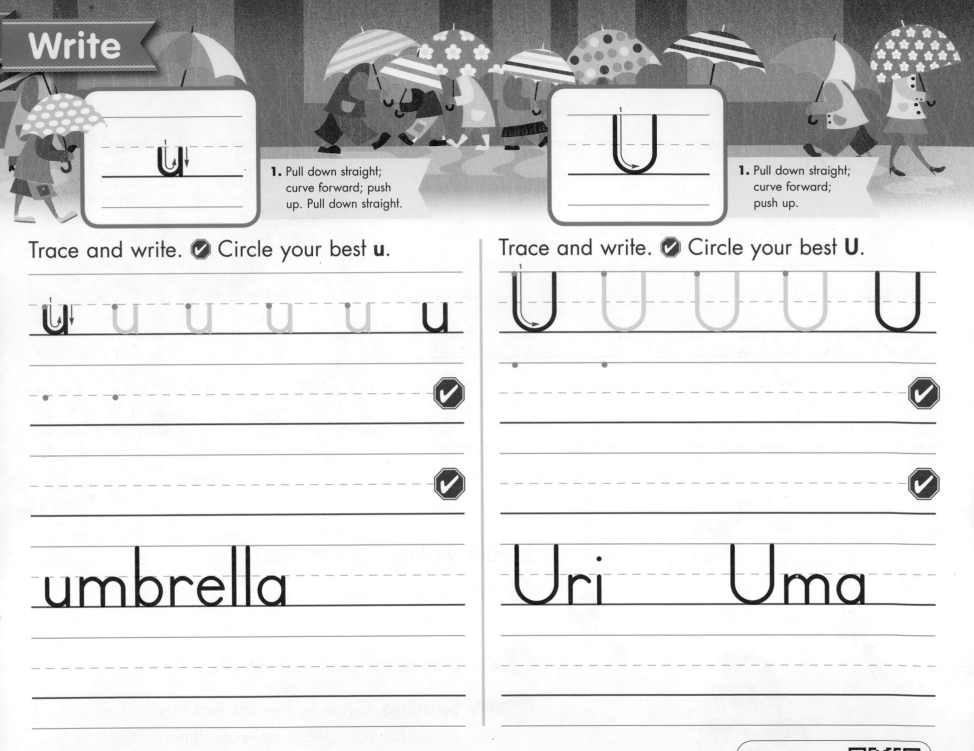

1. Pull down straight; curve forward; push up. Pull down straight.

1. Pull down straight; curve forward; push up.

Trace and write. ✅ Circle your best **u**.

Trace and write. ✅ Circle your best **U**.

u   u   u   u   u   u

U   U   U   U   U

umbrella

Uri   Uma

Write the words.

uncle   us   under   up

Write the sentence.

Use your umbrella now.

What do you use when it rains? Write a sentence to answer the question.

Size Circle your best short letter.

1. Curve back;
curve forward.

1. Curve back;
curve forward.

Trace and write. ✓ Circle your best **s**.

Trace and write. ✓ Circle your best **S**.

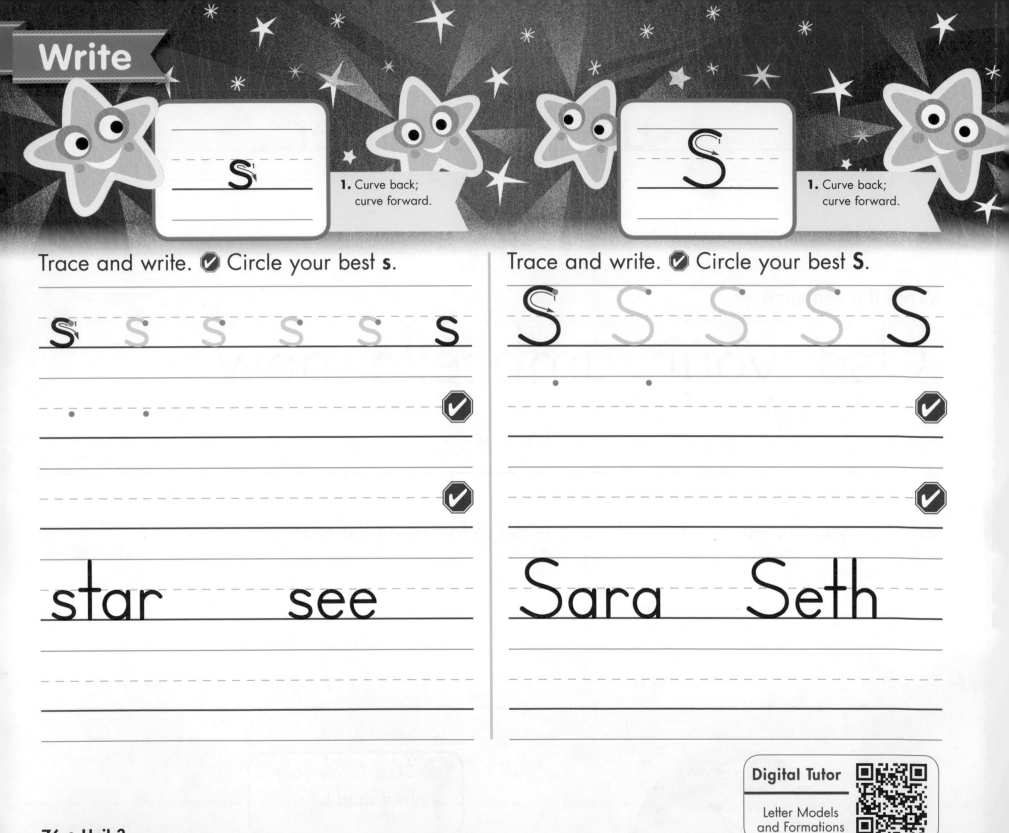

s s s s s s

S S S S S

star   see

Sara   Seth

Digital Tutor

Letter Models
and Formations

Write the words.

said   sun   sit   sofa

Write the sentence.

Should I sing a song?

Write a sentence that tells the name of a song you like to sing.

Spacing Circle two words with good spacing between them.

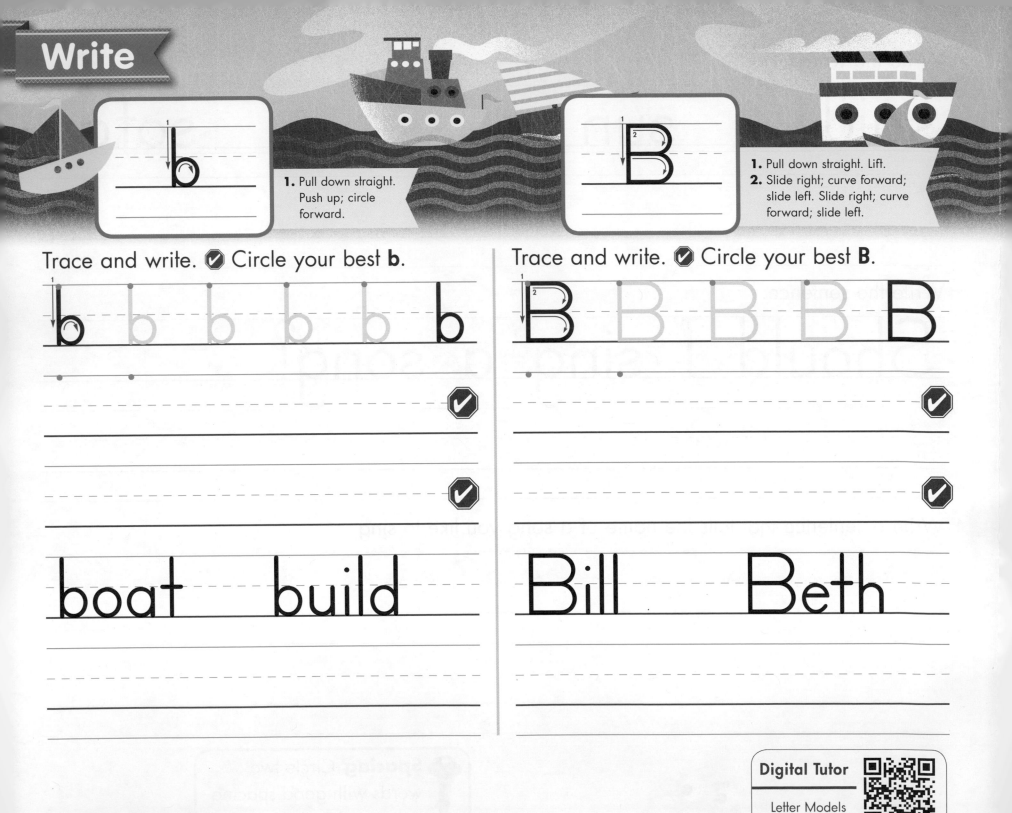

1. Pull down straight. Push up; circle forward.

1. Pull down straight. Lift.
2. Slide right; curve forward; slide left. Slide right; curve forward; slide left.

Trace and write. ✔ Circle your best **b**.

b b b b b b

boat build

Trace and write. ✔ Circle your best **B**.

B B B B B

Bill Beth

Digital Tutor

Letter Models and Formations

Write the words.

bell   baby   been   bring

Write the sentence.

Big books are great!

Write a sentence telling what kind of books you like.

Slant Circle a word you wrote that has good slant.

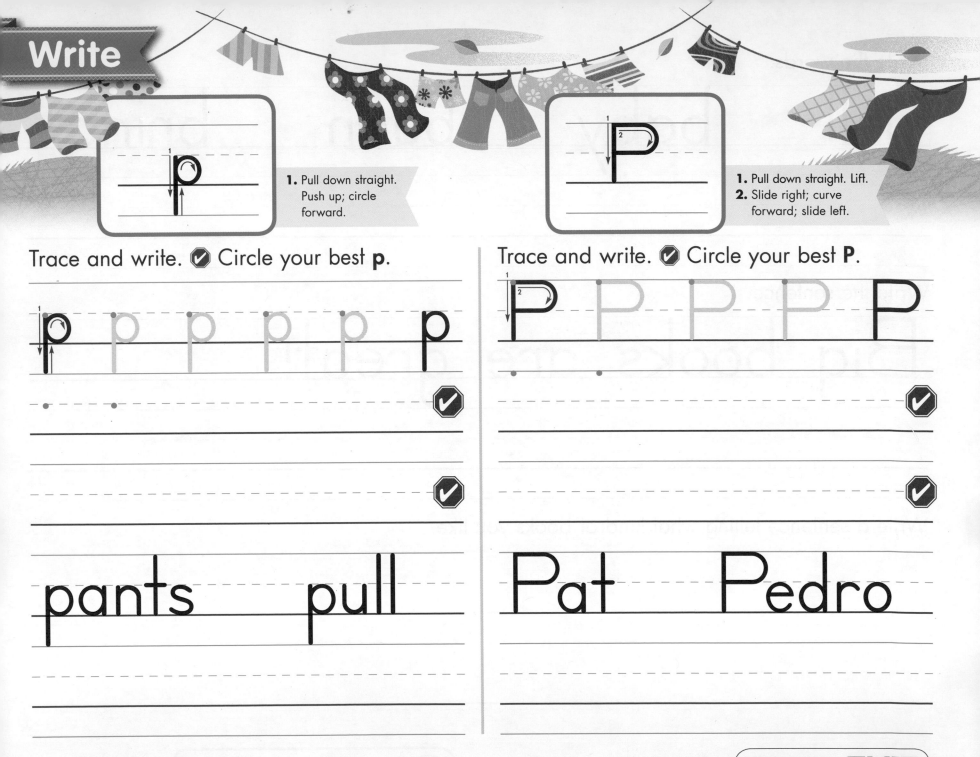

1. Pull down straight. Push up; circle forward.

1. Pull down straight. Lift.
2. Slide right; curve forward; slide left.

Trace and write. ✓ Circle your best **p**.

Trace and write. ✓ Circle your best **P**.

p p p p p p

P P P P P P

pants   pull

Pat   Pedro

Digital Tutor

Letter Models and Formations

Write the words.

pen   pig   push   put

Write the sentence.

Please pass the paper.

Write a sentence that begins with **Please**.

Shape Circle your best
letter that has a l line.

Write the letters.

u u u s s s b b b p p p

U U S S B B P P

Write the words.

bus   pup   cub   cup

Tongue Twisters Write the tongue twisters. Then say them fast.

Bob bakes bread.

Paula pets a pink pig.

Six snakes have snacks.

Write your own tongue twister.

Write

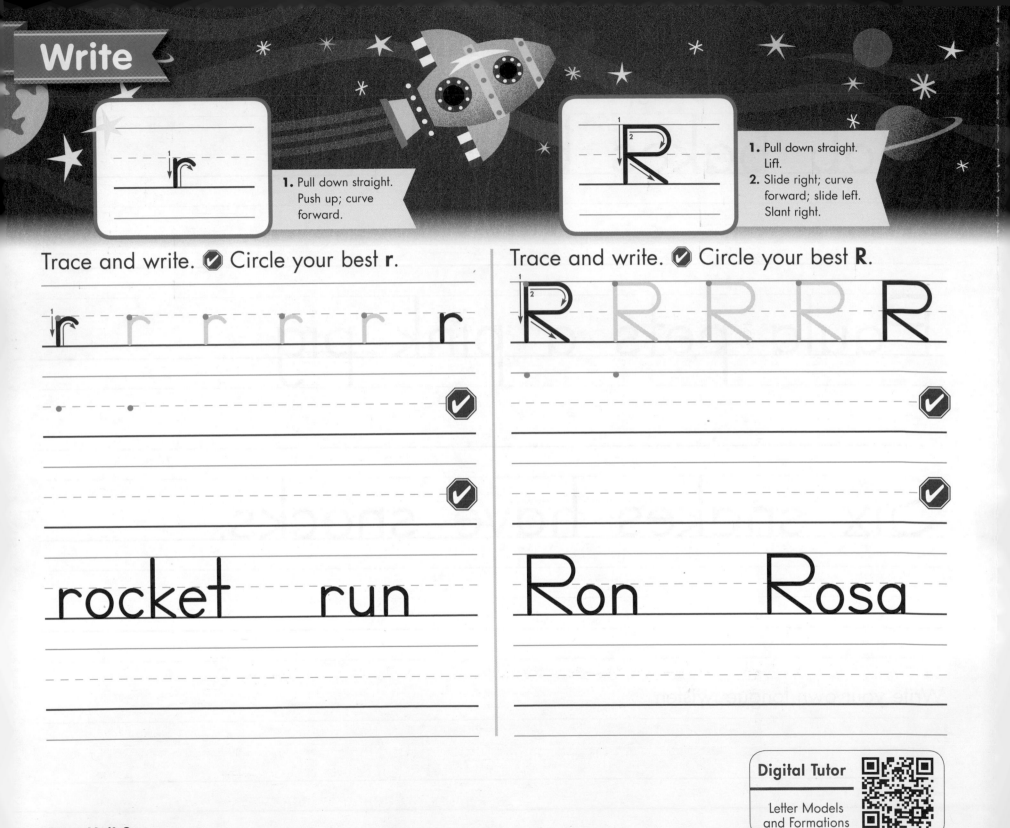

r

1. Pull down straight. Push up; curve forward.

R

1. Pull down straight. Lift.
2. Slide right; curve forward; slide left. Slant right.

Trace and write. ✓ Circle your best **r**.

r r r r r r r

rocket run

Trace and write. ✓ Circle your best **R**.

R R R R R

Ron Rosa

Digital Tutor

Letter Models and Formations

Write the words.

rock   rain   read   ring

Write the sentence.

Read me a story.

Who reads to you? Write a sentence to answer the question.

Size Circle a word you wrote that has good size.

Write

n
1. Pull down straight.
   Push up; curve forward;
   pull down straight.

N
1. Pull down straight.
   Lift.
2. Slant right. Push
   up straight.

Trace and write. ✓ Circle your best **n**.

n   n   n   n   n

nest   need

Trace and write. ✓ Circle your best **N**.

N   N   N   N   N

Nina   Nick

Digital Tutor

Letter Models
and Formations

Write the words.

nine   nail   nap   nod

Write the sentences. Leave the correct spacing between words and sentences.

No napping! Wake up!

Write a sentence that tells how you wake up.

Spacing Circle two letters with good spacing between them.

Write

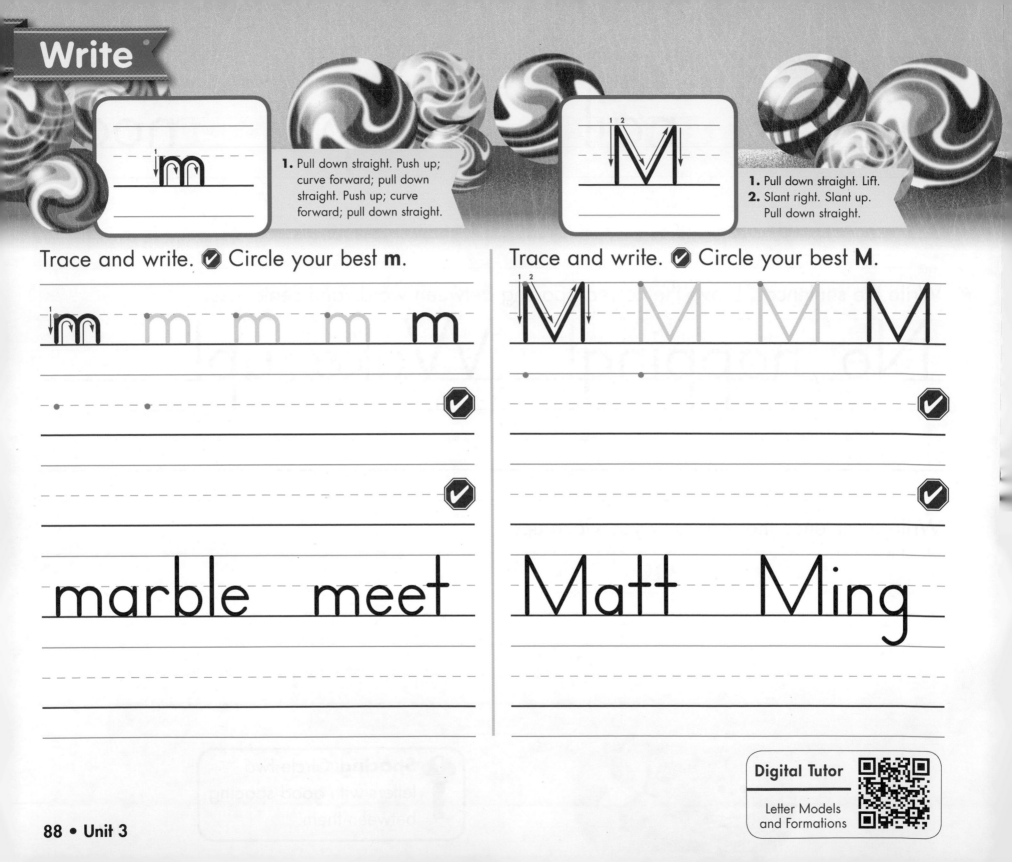

1. Pull down straight. Push up; curve forward; pull down straight. Push up; curve forward; pull down straight.

1. Pull down straight. Lift.
2. Slant right. Slant up. Pull down straight.

Trace and write. ✔ Circle your best **m**.

m m m m m

marble meet

Trace and write. ✔ Circle your best **M**.

M M M M M

Matt Ming

Digital Tutor

Letter Models and Formations

Write the words.

mom   moon   mail   miss

Write the sentence.

My lunch is yummy!

Write a sentence to tell what you like to eat for lunch.

Slant Circle a letter that is straight up and down.

1. Pull down straight.
Push up; curve forward;
pull down straight.

1. Pull down straight. Lift.
2. Pull down straight. Lift.
3. Slide right.

Trace and write. ✓ Circle your best **h**.

h h h h h h

horse   hug

Trace and write. ✓ Circle your best **H**.

H H H H H H

Hailey Hank

Digital Tutor

Letter Models
and Formations

Write the words.

hill house have hop

Write the sentence.

How may I help you?

How do you help others? Write a sentence to answer the question.

Shape Circle a word you wrote that has good shape.

Write the letters.

r r r n n n m m m h h h

R R N N M M H H

Write the words.

name room home horn

To-Do List Write the list of things to do.

1. Return Nate's hat.

2. Make a map.

3. Have a snack.

Write one more thing to do.

4.

Keys to Legibility

Write the rhyming words.
Make your writing easy to read.

rest   nest   rod   nod

rug   mug   rat   mat

nap   map   noon   moon

I see hens in a pen!

Is your writing easy to read?

 **Shape** Circle your best letter that has a I line.

Size Circle your best tall letter.

Spacing Circle two words that have space for your finger between them.

Slant Circle a letter you wrote that is straight up and down.

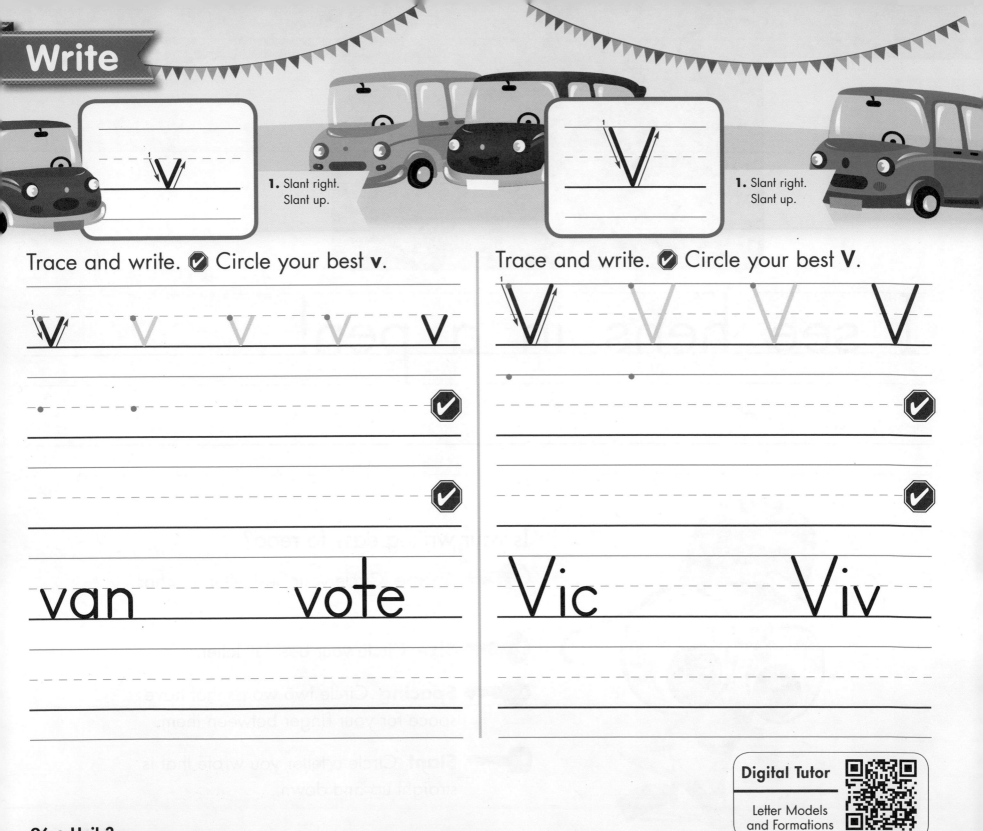

1. Slant right.
Slant up.

1. Slant right.
Slant up.

Trace and write. ✓ Circle your best **v**.

Trace and write. ✓ Circle your best **V**.

van   vote

Vic   Viv

Digital Tutor

Letter Models
and Formations

Write the words.

vest   video   visit   very

Write the sentence.

Violet loves vegetables.

Write a sentence that tells what you love to eat.

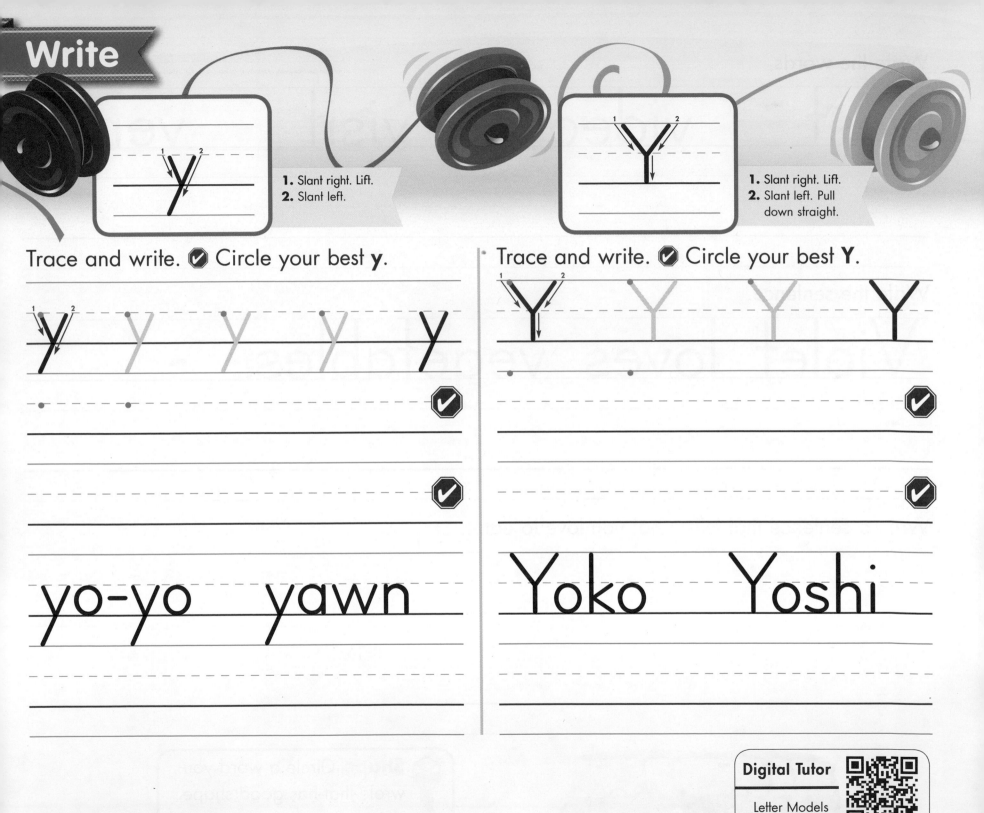

Write

Trace and write. ✓ Circle your best **y**.

1. Slant right. Lift.
2. Slant left.

y   y   y   y   y

yo-yo   yawn

Trace and write. ✓ Circle your best **Y**.

1. Slant right. Lift.
2. Slant left. Pull down straight.

Y   Y   Y   Y   Y

Yoko   Yoshi

Digital Tutor

Letter Models and Formations

Write the words.

yard you yell yes

Write the sentence.

You can play with me.

Write a sentence that tells what games you like to play.

Size Circle your best letter that goes below the baseline.

Write

1. Slant right. Slant up.
Slant right. Slant up.

1. Slant right. Slant up.
Slant right. Slant up.

Trace and write. ✓ Circle your best **w**.

w w w w

wagon wait

Trace and write. ✓ Circle your best **W**.

W W W W

Will Wendy

Digital Tutor

Letter Models
and Formations

Write the words.

winter   word   want   wish

Write the sentence.

Will it snow today?

Write a sentence that tells what the weather is like today.

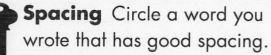

Spacing Circle a word you wrote that has good spacing.

Write the letters.

v   v   v   y   y   y   w   w   w

V   V   V   Y   Y   Y   W   W

Write the words.

your   wave   vet   way

Invitation Write the invitation.

You're Invited to a Party!

When: Friday at 4:00

Where: Valley School

1. Slant right. Lift.
2. Slant left.

1. Slant right. Lift.
2. Slant left.

Trace and write. ✓ Circle your best **x**.

Trace and write. ✓ Circle your best **X**.

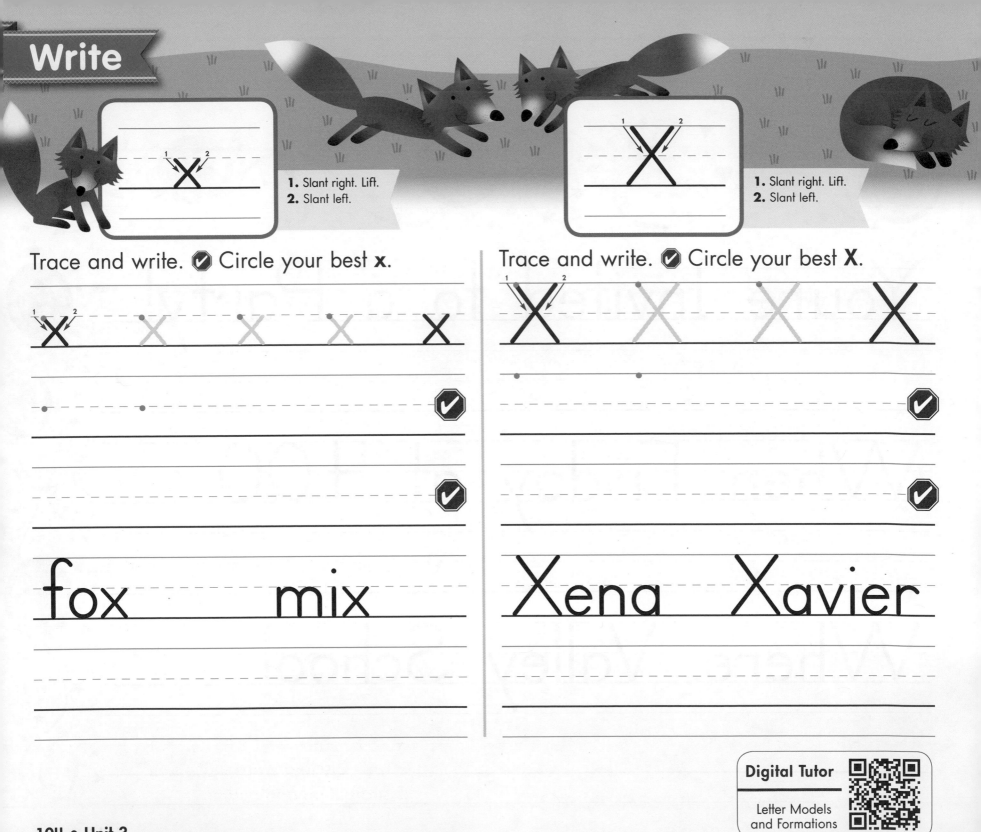

fox   mix

Xena   Xavier

Digital Tutor

Letter Models
and Formations

Write the words.

box   six   taxi   fix

Write the sentence.

Xia draws a fox.

Write a sentence to tell where you would find a fox.

Write

1. Pull down straight. Lift.
2. Slant left. Slant right.

1. Pull down straight. Lift.
2. Slant left. Slant right.

Trace and write. ✓ Circle your best **k**.

k k k k k

kite keep

Trace and write. ✓ Circle your best **K**.

K K K K K

Ken Keisha

Digital Tutor

Letter Models and Formations

Write the words.

kids   keys   kick   kiss

Write the sentence.

Kids like to fly kites.

Write a sentence that tells about other things kids like to do.

Shape Circle your best letter that has a / line.

Write

1. Slide right.
Slant left.
Slide right.

1. Slide right.
Slant left.
Slide right.

Trace and write. ✓ Circle your best **z**.

z z z z z

Trace and write. ✓ Circle your best **Z**.

Z Z Z Z Z

zebra   zip

Zoey   Zach

Digital Tutor

Letter Models
and Formations

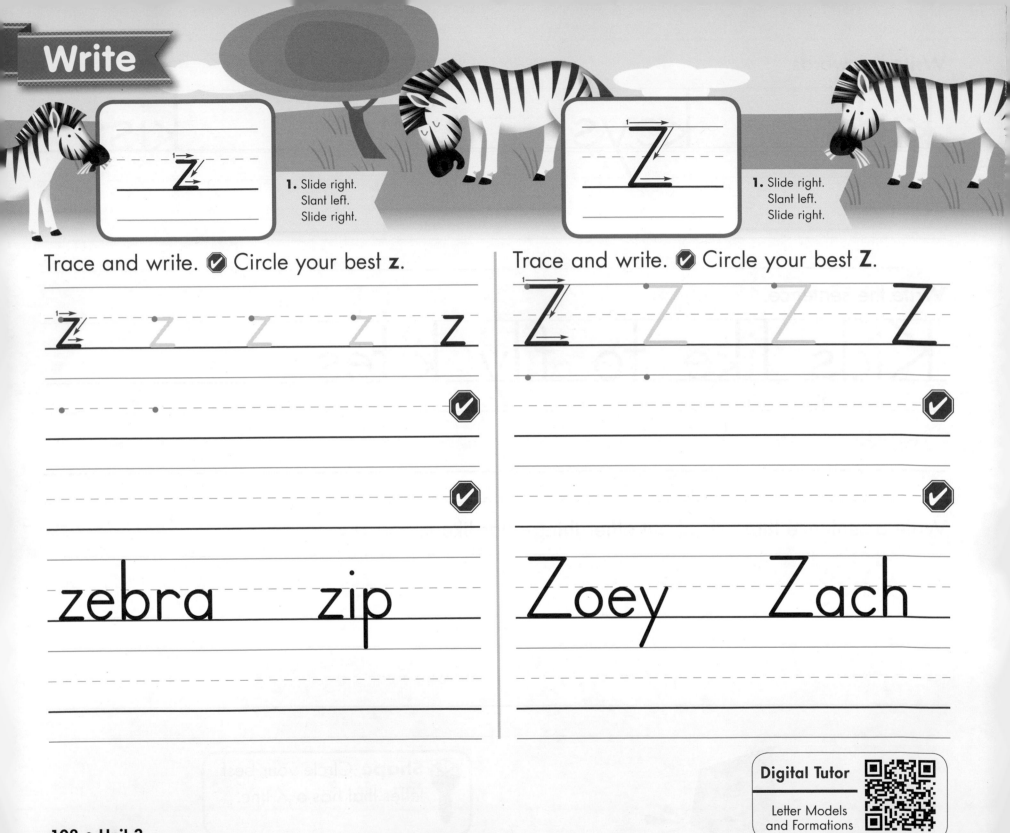

Write the words.

zoo   fuzzy   maze   zoom

Write the sentence.

Z is a zigzag letter.

Write a sentence that tells about things that zigzag.

Size Circle a word you wrote that has good size.

Write the letters.

x x x x   k k k k   z z z z

X X X   K K K   Z Z Z

Write the words.

buzz   zero   next   king

Story Write the sentences.

Mix the batter.

Bake the cookie.

It zooms away.

Write a word that tells something about the Cookie Man.

Keys to Legibility

Write how to get ready for bed.
Make your writing easy to read.

1. Change your clothes.

2. Brush your teeth.

3. Then lie down.

Sweet dreams. ZZZzzz.

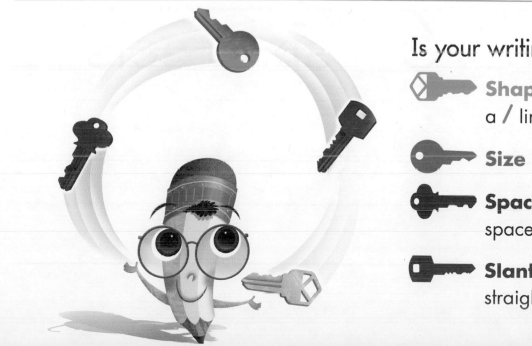

Is your writing easy to read?

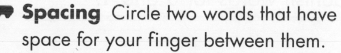 **Shape** Circle your best letter that has a / line.

Size Circle your best short letter.

Spacing Circle two words that have space for your finger between them.

Slant Circle a letter you wrote that is straight up and down.

Handwriting in the Real World

Number Words Write the numerals and the number words in English and Spanish.

1 one   uno

2 two   dos

3 three   tres

4 four   cuatro

5 five   cinco

6 six   seis

Write the Spanish words for **3** and **4**.

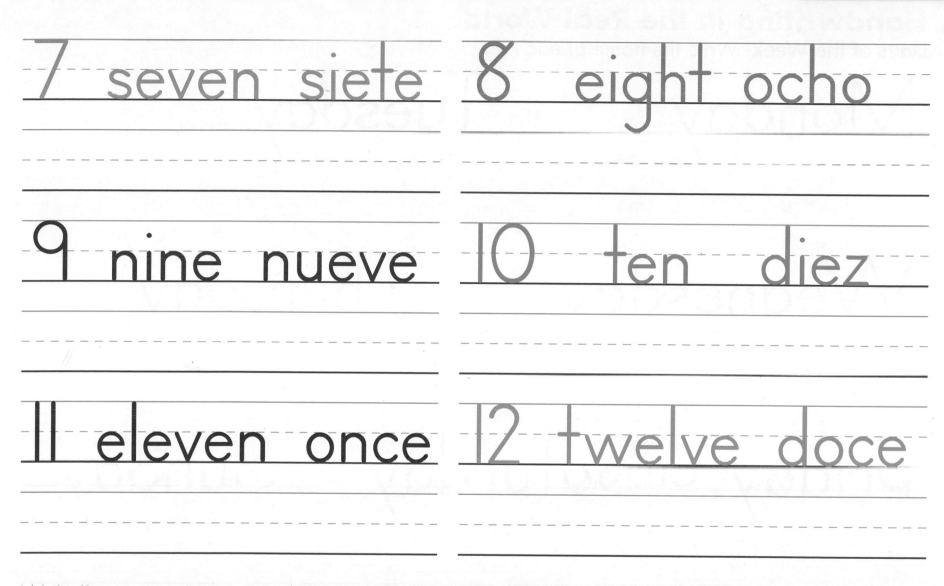

7 seven siete   8 eight ocho

9 nine nueve   10 ten diez

11 eleven once   12 twelve doce

Write the numeral and a number word to tell your age.

Handwriting in the Real World
Days of the Week Write the name of each day.

Monday   Tuesday

Wednesday   Thursday

Friday   Saturday   Sunday

Handwriting in the Real World
Friendly Letter Write to a friend. Finish this letter.

Dear

Today is

Your friend,

Handwriting in the Real World
Months Write the name of each month.

January   February

March   April   May

June   July   August

September   October

November   December

Write the names of two months that have holidays.

Opinion

Book Review Finish this book review.

I read

It was about

I liked it because

Draw something from the book you read.

Apply

Opinion

My Favorite Food Write names of your favorite foods. Then circle the food you like best.

1.

2.

3.

4.

5.

6.

7.

Write the name of your favorite food. Then write at least one reason it is your favorite. Remember to leave space for margins.

My favorite food is

Narrative

Story Retelling Draw the characters and setting of a story you know well. Then write the title of the story.

Title:

Retell the story in your own words. Be sure to include the characters, setting, and important events. Remember to indent the first line of each paragraph you write and leave space for margins.

Narrative

The Best Day Draw a picture of a great day you had.

Write a short story about a time you had a great day. Be sure to include a beginning, a middle, and an ending. Remember to indent the first line of each paragraph you write and leave space for margins.

Informative/Explanatory

How To Think of something you can do well. Write it on the top line. Then explain how to do it with each step in order.

_____

_____

1. _____

2. _____

3. _____

4. _____

5. _____

Sentence Read the sentence below. It includes every letter of the alphabet.

The quick brown fox jumps over the lazy dog.

Write the sentence two times in your best handwriting.

My writing has good	
Shape	☐
Size	☐
Spacing	☐
Slant	☐

Evaluate

Posttest

Write lowercase letters from **a** to **z**.

Write uppercase letters from **A** to **Z**.

Finish the story.

Once when I was little, I went to

My writing has good

- Shape ☐
- Size ☐
- Spacing ☐
- Slant ☐

Credits

Art: Gail Armstrong: Cover; Kevin Zimmer: i, 1, 14, 16, 18, 21, 55, 73, 95, 113; Nancy Gale Carlson/Painted Words: ii (dog, birds), iii (bird), 30–35, 53, 63, 71; Tim Beaumont/Painted Words: ii (star), 66–67, 70 (juice), 74–82, 84–92; Mircea Catusanu/Painted Words: iii (fox), 96–111, 116–119; Bob Masheris/Wilkinson Studios: 6, 8, 10–12, 15–17; Gary Krejca/Wilkinson Studios: 20, 22–29; Bernard Adnet/Craven Design: 36–52, 56–62, 64–65, 68–69, 70 (goats, quilt)

Photos: © George C. Anderson Photography, Inc.: 4, 5; © iStock.com/Fernando Delvalle: 55; © iStock.com/fstop123 (grandfather and grandson): 73; © iStock.com/enviromantic (picture frame): 73; © iStock.com/liveslow: 95; © iStock.com/jianying yin: 113